Harlequin Romance

2265

1.25

The Winds of Heaven

MARGARET WAY

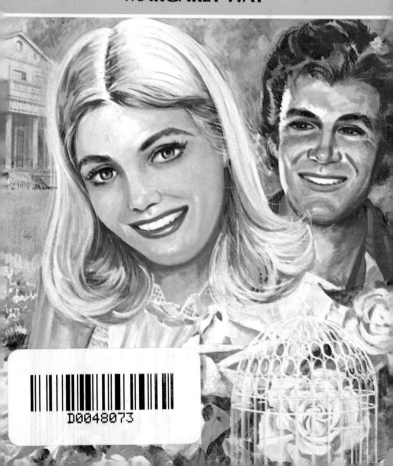

"You little fool! I did try to warn you."

Marc moved then like a panther while Amanda froze in torment. He pulled her to him with irresistible strength. "I can't let you go now!"

"Oh, no!" she whispered vehemently, terrified now of what might happen. No one she had ever met had such power to excite such deep and changing emotions in her.

"You can't escape me," he said softly. "Do you know what it's like, Amanda, to find no water in the desert? No life. No love. No woman to pledge the kind of passion I want!"

"This is madness!" she said breathlessly, and then her stricken sigh faded into the wind as his lips covered hers....

The Winds of Heaven

by

MARGARET WAY

Harlequin Books

TORONTO • LONDON • NEW YORK • AMSTERDAM
SYDNEY • HAMBURG • PARIS

Original hardcover edition published in 1979
by Mills & Boon Limited

ISBN 0-373-02265-4

Harlequin edition published June 1979

PRINTED IN U.S.A.

CHAPTER ONE

IT was almost the end of surgery on that Saturday morning when Marc Chandler pushed through the front door. Amanda glanced up automatically, certain it would be another patient, then she felt herself stiffen in jarring shock.

He came directly towards her, a strong, disturbing man. 'How are you, Amanda?'

There seemed to be a curl of sarcasm or challenge in that dark, vibrant voice. 'Fine, thank you, Mr Chandler,' she said quietly. 'If you want to see Doctor McGilvray, he's almost through. Shall I buzz him for you?'

'Don't bother!' He half turned away from her, as arrogant and commanding as only he knew how to be. 'If you wait on for a few minutes, I'll drive you home.'

He didn't smile as he said it and Amanda found herself flushing. 'It doesn't matter, really. The bus is at the door.'

Light streamed through the big windows, illuminating him clearly. A tall man, lean and hard, even a little frightening, though his face was harshly handsome. Hair and eyes were both black as midnight and his skin was tanned to a dark copper. Marc Chandler, a man with whom everyone was very respectful and careful.

'You dislike me, don't you?' he demanded abruptly.

'Of course I don't!' She was forced into lying, her

green gaze locked and her flawless young skin flushing deeper.

'Then that's fortunate!' The chiselled mouth thinned deliberately and Amanda was conscious of the faint tremble in her hands.

'If you'll excuse me,' she said, catching herself up, 'I have a few accounts to finish.'

'Go right ahead!' he murmured, his dark face already remote.

She felt more than saw him cross to the window and look out, then she bent over her typewriter. The slightest contact she had with this man always unnerved her, yet she couldn't afford to offend him. Like everything else in the town, the Medical Centre benefited greatly from the generosity of Marc Chandler. It had been almost entirely rebuilt, no longer the dark and melancholy place it had once been, but a place to admire, light-filled and air-conditioned as befitting the tropics. Even Doctor McGilvray had little to complain about these days, with a first-class team and a whole new range of equipment. Not that the dear old pet was awash with gratitude, for which Amanda admired him. He was glad of such a splendid patron, of course, but Doctor McGilvray considered Marc Chandler had a clear duty to the community just as he himself had a duty towards the sick people of the town. The Chandlers were the first family of the district, owners of the Mount Regina copper mine that had once yielded gold, rich and powerful, the centre of everything.

And how I dislike him! Amanda thought, shamed by her own illogicality. She scarcely knew him, except as a power and an influence. Once, almost two years ago, he had proposed sending her south to university.

Amanda was a fit subject for charity, orphaned at eight and in the care of an elderly aunt. There had been little money to further her studies even when her scholastic record had been excellent. Amanda was a clever girl, but never for one moment did she consider taking charity from Marc Chandler. Aunt Clare had agreed with her, even if it had broken her heart; there simply wasn't the money. Now Aunt Clare too had gone and Amanda was alone in a large old rambling house and very glad of her job at the Centre. If she had been forced to shrug off her ambitions, well, some things could never be no matter how one struggled. Unconsciously she sighed, and the tall man at the window turned to stare at her.

'What's the matter?' he demanded.

'I was thinking.'

'About what might have been?'

'No!' she denied, a little wretchedly.

'It sounds very much like it to me.'

She shook her head determinedly. 'I think I'll just ring through. Doctor McGilvray wouldn't like me to keep you waiting.'

Even as she spoke there was a murmur of voices, then Doctor McGilvray and his patient walked through to the foyer. The doctor's shrewd glance flicked Amanda's face, then he patted Mrs Marshall's shoulder while that lady darted off with a quick, avid glance at Marc Chandler.

'How are you, Marc?' The two men moved together to shake hands. 'Good to see you.'

'If you could spare me a few moments?'

'Why, certainly.' The faded blue eyes moved on to Amanda. 'Take yourself off, dear. Go away and enjoy yourself. You deserve a medal for handling those bush kids. The mother is a perfect fool!'

Amanda smiled at him and Marc Chandler turned back to catch the edge of that uncomplicated sweetness. 'I'd like you to wait, Amanda, if you would.'

It was plainly an order and even Doctor McGilvray seemed to nod his silver head with its upstanding aureole.

'Very well!' Amanda was still vastly uncomfortable under that brilliant black regard.

He inclined his head and Amanda had the distinct impression that he had never been crossed in his life. Certainly not by a woman. She watched both men disappear, then she began to tidy up the splendid boomerang-shaped desk. She had a lot to be thankful for. Her job as a receptionist paid well and the work was far from frustrating. She was very conscious and grateful that she brought some measure of ease to the patients with her natural sympathy and friendliness of manner, and Doctor McGilvray, especially, counted on her in many small ways. He had brought her into the world as he had most of the town's younger generation and he had attended her dear, dying aunt. It made a strong bond. It seemed funny that Marc Chandler would want to drive her home. Perhaps he was sorry for her. Something like that. . . .

By the time she had covered the typewriter the slim, languid figure of Doctor Courtney's last patient drifted down the corridor. She looked at Amanda rather stupidly, waved her fingers, then walked with purposeful vagueness to the door. Most of the women patients had a crush on Rob Courtney. That was the danger with good-looking young doctors.

Rob came through to the front desk a few moments later, frowning as though something was half irritating him. 'Still here?'

'I am.'

'Could be you've changed your mind about that dinner invitation?' he said to her, his hazel eyes searching her face.

'Lord, no!' Amanda smiled at him.

'You'll like it!'

'I'm sure I would. The thing is I don't really like to mix business with pleasure.'

Rob groaned and made something of a performance of it. 'As though everyone doesn't! You could easily say yes.'

Amanda appeared to consider. 'Half your trouble is women who fling themselves at you.'

'How interesting!' He half smiled at her. 'Put it down to the human condition. Sure you won't change your mind?'

'Sure,' she answered with calm.

Rob sighed and looked about him. 'Anyone else here?'

'Doctor McGilvray has Marc Chandler with him.'

'Good grief!' Rob returned with some force. 'Surely not as a patient?'

'A private conversation, I think.'

'I'm struck all of a heap. Fancy the Great Man coming down here!' There was a short pause and Rob looked towards the front door. 'And where is his extremely beautiful wife?'

'Not with him.' Amanda moved briskly.

'Isn't she just beautiful?' Rob persisted, rather maliciously, Amanda thought.

'I haven't seen her in a long time. But yes, she is beautiful, the most beautiful woman I've ever seen. But then I don't believe for one moment that anything in Marc Chandler's home isn't perfect.'

'Then you haven't been paying attention to all the gossip!' Rob said slyly, his eyes intent on her face.

'That's right!' she lifted her head to assure him. 'I don't listen to gossip, particularly when it's ugly!'

Rob made jeering sounds and caught at her chin. 'Now that's a revealing remark. People right up there in a shrine are natural targets for gossip. Who hasn't heard the curious tales about the lovely neurotic Caro? It's common knowledge the marriage isn't a great big success.'

The sensitive Amanda found the conversation distasteful. 'That's none of our business, surely?'

'I'd say it was pretty good to know even the high and mighty have troubles.'

'You don't like him?' Amanda asked.

'I admire him like crazy!' Rob said over-heartily. 'Don't take it so hard. Anyway, I like my job. You're the one who puzzles me. Dressed up all shiny and expensive you'd make even the lovely Caro look passée, yet you're not interested in men.'

'By the name of Rob, you mean?' she parried lightly.

'You don't go out!'

'I do so. Often.'

'What, to a concert or the movies or in a party. That's terrible!' He lifted his hand and caught at her hair and it fell out of its confining coil into a shining pale gold ribbon over her shoulder. 'Even the way you do your hair is old-maidish!'

'It's sensible for an office!' she said, and ducked to one side.

'Mandy?' he asked, and his voice sounded less sure of itself, more appealing. 'Can't you believe I just want to get to know you better? You're a beautiful girl and you can't go on living such a quiet life.'

'Is that how you think of me?' She shook back her hair, looking around for the hair slide.

'Don't be too clever, pet. A woman isn't supposed to be.'

'Fiddlesticks!' she returned somewhat bitterly. 'This is irritating, you know. I hate being untidy.'

Rob's wide mouth twisted and he moved his shoe off the silver hair slide. 'Aren't you just the teeniest bit afraid life is going to pass you by?'

'I'm nineteen years old!' she protested.

'I know,' he said in some exasperation, and bent down for the clip. 'You're such a solemn baby. I want to teach you to enjoy yourself.'

'Please, Rob,' she held out her hand for the hair ornament, 'Mr Chandler is going to give me a lift home and I don't think he'll be impressed by long, flowing locks!'

'The hell he won't!' Rob expostulated, and his smooth good-looking face hardened into a taut mask. 'You're laughable, do you know that? There isn't a man alive that could resist such spectacular hair.'

'That's ridiculous!'

'*Is* it?'

The rest of what Rob was going to say was lost, because Marc Chandler appeared soundlessly in the doorway, his black eyes fixed on them, alive with diamond-hard and cynical intelligence, although his expression, as usual, was quite unreadable.

'Why, Mr Chandler!' said Rob, and it came out like a greeting for Caesar.

'How are you, Courtney?' Marc Chandler moved across the foyer like the Prince of Darkness, holding out a hand which Rob took and shook with a remarkable show of pleasure and a treacherous duplicity.

'I've been looking forward to thanking you for all the new equipment. You can't know what it means to us. A miracle!'

'I'm glad I'm in a position to help.'

'Yes, indeed!' Rob returned equably. 'I believe I have to thank you too for my entrée into the Country Club.'

'My pleasure!' Marc Chandler inclined his head suavely, but Amanda was painfully aware of his hard, measuring glance. It didn't seem to matter a whit to Rob, who continued to stand there and smile.

'If you're ready, Amanda?' That curious blend of challenge and an underlying antagonism was in the dark voice again.

'Thank you.' She gathered up her things, wishing she had the self-confidence to sweep out before him instead of hesitating rather shyly. 'Goodbye, Doctor Courtney.'

'*Rob*. It's no secret!' Rob's laugh was low and strangely misleading.

There was a touch of irony in Marc Chandler's dark eyes. 'I'll see you again, Courtney.'

'Perhaps at the Club. They tell me you're absolutely stunning at any sport one can mention.'

'I used to be. I have very little time these days—I have some plans for the mine.'

'Marvellous!' Rob's voice implied that he knew all

about Big Business. 'The whole town of Chandler depends on you.'

'Occasionally I'd like to get away from it.' Marc Chandler put out his arm and opened the door. 'After you, Amanda.'

She heard Rob calling goodbye, then they were out in the blinding sunlight, rinsing her hair to silver-gilt. She put up a hand to pull it back into some semblance of its former cool elegance and the man beside her said rather bluntly:

'Leave it. I'm not going to strangle you.'

'Such a thought never crossed my mind.'

'Then tell me the meaning of that inexcusable little expression.'

The colour bloomed in her cheeks again, then as swiftly died. 'I didn't in the least mind going home in the bus.'

He ignored her. 'I didn't think you'd have to, with Courtney so obviously dancing attendance.'

Amanda looked out over the shimmering street towards where the big Mercedes was parked. 'Don't please misread the situation. I only see Doctor Courtney at work.'

'I know that.'

She turned her head and looked at him. 'I'm surprised.'

'Which just goes to show how very young you are. I've spies everywhere. People tell me everything whenever they've got a chance.'

'How dreadful!' she said, and meant it.

He shrugged his wide shoulders as though he cared little for her opinion, then he went swiftly to the passenger side of the pale yellow Mercedes and opened the door for her. She bent her head, murmuring a polite thank-you, and slid into the bucket seat, enjoying the expensive smell of plush leather despite herself.

After a minute he joined her and the big car suddenly seemed very much smaller, almost claustrophobic.

'Relax!' he said almost casually. 'It's not my aim to strike terror into you.'

'Would it be any help at all to say I'm perfectly calm?'

His black eyes touched her face briefly, then they were moving out of the angled parking bay into the wide main street of the town towards the bridge that spanned the broad, deep river. Chandler was a very pleasant town, largely dominated by the Chandlers and dependent for its prosperity on the rich Mount Regina copper mine, an open-cut operation, a healthy distance from the rapidly developing town.

It was November, and the trees that lined the streets and the banks of the river were breathtakingly beautiful with flower: the poincianas, the jarcarandas and the showiest members of the pea family, the magnificent bauhinias, their bare branches covered in orchid-like blooms. One of the delights of living in the tropics, Amanda considered, was the luxuriant landscape, and Chandler boasted many beautiful parks and gardens. There were even black and white swans gliding under the bridge and the lawn that ran right down to the water reeds was jade green.

Marc Chandler seemed wrapped in his thoughts, so Amanda too maintained a silence. Perhaps when she got home she would cool off at the picnic area of the lake. It was hot and still enough for a thunderstorm late afternoon, but she would be safely back by then.

Lightning terrified her and always had done since the time she was twelve and the great fig in the school grounds had been razed to the ground, trapping and killing one of the women teachers. Always in her deep subconscious she remembered the scene and the screams of the girls. It was impossible to live in the tropics and not conquer her fear, though it remained with her and showed itself in a kind of abstraction and a sick look in the eyes.

Marc Chandler had to repeat his question before she heard him. 'I beg your pardon. I was daydreaming.' Contrition flared in her green eyes.

'I said, are you happy, Amanda?'

'Surely it's quite apparent that I am?' She sat more erect, willow-slim, young skin like a pearl, her expression and the set of her narrow shoulders revealing her youth.

'I didn't mean to hurt you, rather I want to discuss something with you. A change of job, something you can do for me.'

Her eyes probed his dark profile. It looked deadly serious, even ruthless. 'Undoubtedly it has something to do with your visit to Doctor McGilvray?'

'Yes.'

He swung the car from the highway and they went like the wind, taking the river road where all the first families lived. 'But we're going the wrong way!' Amanda flung out a shaky hand.

'You'll be home soon enough,' he said, so abruptly it was like a slap in the face. 'I want a little privacy to speak to you, not a whole street full of gossiping neighbours.' His black eyes touched hers with that damaging insolence. 'O.K.?'

'If you say so.' She turned her head away so he couldn't see her face. The great forest of shade trees met overhead and formed a cool green tunnel for all that travelled this exclusive road. Her hair was falling like silk about her face, but she didn't dare put up a hand. She had to remember to sit still and do what she was told. Marc Chandler was a superior being and he had something to ask of her. It nearly made her laugh.

Past the bend in the river they slid in under the trees, keeping on going until they came down on the shoreline. On the opposite bank, like some impossible vision, was the great white mansion John Phillips Chandler, Marc's great-grandfather, had built in the days when the mine, named after his young wife Regina, operated as a goldmine.

It belonged in its beautiful shadowed setting as surely as the magnificent old shade trees that surrounded it and protected its chaste white walls from the burning sun. A fabulous house of soaring columns that made Amanda's heart lift in spite of her tension.

'How perfect!' she sighed as though she could never intrude there.

'A house is only a house!' he returned rather curtly. 'It's people that count.'

'I'm glad you think so!' It was out before she could control the wayward impulse.

'Go on.'

'I'm sorry!' She let her head droop forward almost penitently. 'What was it you wanted to speak to me about?'

'You know I have a daughter?'

'Yes.' Surprised, she turned her luminous eyes to

him. 'I've seen her a number of times. A lovely-looking child.'

'She's also rather delicate,' he said grimly. 'Highly strung. Which is one reason I want you to come to us as a kind of governess-companion. Karin has a cousin too, young Philip. You'd be expected to look after him as well. Pip is six, my sister's child. Jennifer and her husband will be overseas for about six months and they don't want to take Pip into the European winter. He suffers from bronchitis on and off and he voted to stay with me. As you know, he has any number of relations to go to, but he's very fond of his grandmother, my mother, and Four Winds is her home as much as mine.'

She stared at him afraid she was being caught in a steel trap. 'Why *me*?'

'For obvious reasons, Amanda. I know you. I know your background. You're a clever girl and you're a lady. I've considered this very seriously and I've spoken to Doctor McGilvray about it. He'll be sorry to lose you, of course, but he sees in you qualities of compassion that I need. You're highly competent and un-complaining and you're very diplomatic.'

'In short, I'm sufficiently respectable to be allowed into the Big House!'

'The doctor said you were tactful. *I* didn't!'

'I can't!' she said.

'Why not?'

'Please don't try to override me. I'm perfectly happy where I am now. In any case, wouldn't Mrs Chandler want to hire me? At least see me first.'

'My wife or my mother?'

'Both!' she said, feeling worn out.

'My mother agrees with me in everything. She always

has done. We just happen to think alike. My wife takes little interest in anything these days. Karin's birth was difficult and she has never fully recovered. She may not take to you, but she won't say anything.'

'To please you?'

'That isn't nice, Amanda!' he said, and his white teeth snapped. 'I suppose you've been listening to gossip.'

'I suppose I have. One doesn't *want* to, but people can't stop talking about the Chandlers.'

'Don't I know it! Society is loaded against the rich or the famous or both. One false move and you're gone.'

'I imagine it has its advantages!' she said dryly.

'Look at me, Amanda.'

She met his eyes—almost. She was determined not to be led by this hard, disturbing man.

'Do you still hold it against me for offering you— charity, wasn't it?'

'You told me you had spies. No, I don't, Mr Chandler. The thing is I don't think I'd be happy in your household.'

His black brows drew together so he looked dangerous. 'Who's asking you to be happy? Hasn't it struck you that nobody's happy? You weren't happy as a schoolgirl with an outsize chip on your shoulder. Your father worked for the mine. He was one of our best engineers. He wasn't on a business trip when he came down in the rain forest, but he could easily have been. We owed you something, but you wouldn't take it.'

'And I'm glad of it!' There was a bitter tang to her sweet clear voice. 'Idiot that I was!'

'You shouldn't mind so much.'

'Oh, don't!' There was a faint throbbing in her

temples and the sun streaming through the trees made her hair more silver than gold. 'I've never asked, but did you nominate me for the new Centre?'

'Another thing you can't forgive?'

'*Did* you?' She tilted her head to stare at him.

'Does it matter?' he said almost implacably. 'I'm waiting for your answer, Amanda. I'm a busy man.'

'I can see that!' she retorted, her calm snapping. 'You've been riding roughshod over people all your life.'

'Such a little *bitch*, when you look like an angel.' He leaned forward and switched on the engine. 'Perhaps you'll change your mind. You won't get your job back at the Centre.'

She wanted to cry out, but she mustn't, and as she met his eyes she saw in them the black, ironic humour. 'That's what you expected, isn't it?' He was steering, reversing with one hand, and she was vaguely conscious that he was cutting a perfect path through the trees.

'I'm sorry I can't help you,' she said, 'but I think the whole thing's fantastic. I've had very little to do with children.'

'You're little more than a child yourself.' He brought the bonnet of the car around and they were back on the road again. 'Besides, didn't I hear the Doc complimenting you on the way you handled the Walker kids? Our kids are saints compared to that. Karin's lessons have suffered because of periodic bursts of sickness, one childhood malady after the other. She needs someone just like you, someone who can be a friend to her as well as a teacher.'

'So you're asking for your daughter?'

'I'm begging!' he said harshly, the cleft very deep in his chin.

'Well, that could win a lot of people over.'

'Quite true. But *you*, Amanda?' His brilliant black eyes glittered with an odd expression.

'I love all children and I understand how you feel, but you could be very much mistaken in thinking I could cope, even in thinking your wife would accept me as Karin's governess.'

'Then I have to reassure you there's absolutely no way she can alter my decision.'

'*Mine*, surely?' She looked at him as though he greatly puzzled her.

'Never mind. Think about it. I'll give you until Monday.' He had hardened in an instant and Amanda shrank back in her seat. There was a great strength underlying that taut, lean body, a passionate nature kept hard in check. He was, she realised with an appalled thrill, a dangerous, exciting man. Could that be the reason after all why she didn't want to enter his household? A sense of self-preservation? Not that those brilliant black eyes had ever been known to rove. He was a man of iron control and after all she was just an ordinary young girl. She had no good reason to be so distrustful.

They drove in silence to the rambling old wide-verandahed home that had once belonged to Amanda's grandparents. She supposed socially it fell into the middle bracket, but it was still a long way from the river road. She was intelligent, she had a cool, patrician face, but she was thinking Mrs Caroline Chandler might bitterly resent her.

'This house is too big for you,' Marc said suddenly. 'Too hard to maintain.'

'It's all I've got.'

He stopped the engine and turned to her. 'I'm prepared to pay you well, Amanda. Far more than you're getting now. Perhaps in six months or so Karin will have shown a big improvement and you'll be much better off financially. What you earn you keep. You'll be living entirely free, as part of the family.'

'But surely that won't work?' She had an instant vision of the imperious Caroline looking down the long dining-room table at her.

'I hate snobs. Any way up!' he said bluntly.

Her green eyes with their dark thick lashes looked quite lost. 'I'm trying to understand, but I can't. You're proposing to pay me well for a position that traditionally pays very little.'

'You'll earn it!' he said, and there was a certain grim humour in his voice. 'I understand you've been studying externally at night. You could with what you save, plus a bonus study full-time for a year. Perhaps complete your course.'

'I could lose my freedom.'

'What freedom? Keeping this house and yourself must be costing you all you've got.' There were points of light in the midnight-dark eyes. 'All I'm asking you to do is take an interest in my small daughter, for which I'll pay you well. You'll live in the lap of luxury, and you must be a very extraordinary young woman if you resent that, and at the end of your term of employment you'll be closer to realising your own ambitions.'

'Perhaps!' She felt awkward and uncertain, a fearful gauche schoolgirl instead of a competent young woman who had been fending for herself for most of her life. 'I'll think very seriously about it.'

'There's nothing else *for* you to do,' he said rather brutally. 'I'll have the house shut up and the grounds maintained until you're ready to come back again. Believe me, Amanda, you're needed at Four Winds.'

There was a moment of silence while Amanda held herself rigidly away from him. There was something magnetic about the man, something overwhelming. Waves of scented jasmine reached out for her. 'I've lived in this town all my life.'

'And we've all watched you grow. Everyone knows your good qualities, Amanda.'

'I'm not nearly the angel you imagine me to be.'

He laughed and it was an extraordinarily attractive sound with an undercurrent of mockery. Their eyes caught and held. 'Off you go,' he said crisply. 'I have work waiting for me a mile high.'

She got out of the car and stood standing beside it, a tall, slender girl, with long graceful limbs.

'Shall I ring you, or what?'

'You'd never get through to me!' He flickered a glance down the drowsy street that was nevertheless listening. 'I'll ring you at the Clinic.'

'Goodbye, and thank you for bringing me home!' She peered in at him, her hair like a waterfall and her green eyes the same colour as the shallows of the lake.

'Feel better now?'

'What do you mean?'

'Goodbye, Amanda,' he said sardonically. 'Perhaps I should take you up to the house so you could be sure what you're letting yourself in for. Anyway, we can arrange that on Monday.'

'You sound as if I've no chance at all,' she complained.

'In a way. You'd better go in now. I think I can hear your phone ringing—probably one of the neighbours. By the way, Amanda, Doctor McGilvray told me you're intensely loyal. I value that. Most people don't know how to give it at all, women especially!'

She could think of nothing to say to him, and anyway it didn't matter. He sketched a brief salute, then drove away without looking back, while Amanda continued to stare along the road disbelievingly. If she accepted a position in Marc Chandler's household it could make a drastic change to her life.

CHAPTER TWO

IT *was* her phone ringing, and when she didn't answer it rang again within fifteen minutes.

'Mandy?' The tone was decidedly proprietorial.

'Yes, Rob.'

'Where the devil have you been? I've been ringing for the best part of an hour.'

I was outside in the garden,' she lied. In the little gilded mirror above the phone she caught sight of her face. It looked different. Not the bone structure, but the expression. She looked lit up, incandescent.

'Mandy, are you still there?'

'Of course, Rob.'

'Listen, darling,' he said pleadingly, 'be a good girl and have dinner with me tonight. I want no woman's company but yours. I'm a reformed character. We'll go to the Country Club, terribly posh and all that. You'll enjoy it for a change. All sorts of people will be there, the Chandlers and the Chandlers' friends and relations. I mean, this is their world and it's fascinating for us outsiders. Do say you'll come. I even spoke to Doc and he said you were a silly girl to knock me back.'

'In any case, I haven't a suitable dress.'

'Oh, don't give me that, for God's sake. You'd look good in a hacked-off gunny sack.'

She gave a small gurgle of laughter and his voice freshened into confidence. 'How good, how sweet, what a kind heart you have. Shall I pick you up about eightish?'

She reached up and tucked her loose blonde hair behind her ear. 'All right, you win!'

'See how nice it's going to be!' he laughed. 'I feel wonderful now. Please, I'm sorry to be a busybody, but what did Chandler have to say?'

'I think we spoke of politics.'

'Liar. All right, you won't tell, but at least I'll get it out of you tonight. 'Bye, sweet, see you soon!'

Amanda put the phone down and gave her reflected image a sharp glance. There was an odd feeling inside her like a hidden wildness, and she had never been wild. All her life she had to work hard and above all behave herself, because Aunt Clare had been elderly though wonderfully devoted and Amanda had never wished to cause her the slightest concern. Always Aunt Clare had been proud of her, her achievements, her cool blonde good looks. Now she was filled with the uncomfortable feeling that she didn't know herself at all. Womanlike, she walked through to her bedroom to consider her evening clothes. There was only one dress really that came anywhere near suitable, but at least she knew she had looked good in it.

Hours later she faced Rob across a corner table at the Chandler Country Club. There were many other clubs in the town, of course, but this one was reserved for the élite and obviously one had to have more than money to get into it. Rob, as an up-and-coming young doctor, had not been considered eligible until Marc Chandler had given the unofficial nod. After that, no one dreamed of blackballing him. Anyway, he played an excellent game of tennis, squash and golf and, genuine sportsmen aren't all that easy to come by.

Tonight the club was about three quarters filled with

older, very sophisticated people and waiters in tight black trousers and clipped white jackets circled the beautifully appointed main dining room bowing and taking orders for dinner and drinks. Amanda refused a pre-dinner drink firmly but pleasantly; she wasn't used to alcohol and she had no plan to make a spectacle of herself. Rob ordered a very dry Martini and when the waiter had gone half leaned across the table to whisper:

'Swanky place, isn't it? Nothing like improving oneself.'

'Are you sure you've got the money?'

'Careful, darling. Don't speak of it now. What a funny little thing you are! Very moral. Anyway, you look ravishing. I can't take my eyes off you!'

'That's particularly reassuring!' she smiled at him. 'I don't feel nearly so smart as I did!' Her ankle-length green jersey fitted her beautifully, but it was very plain and quite inexpensive. Her only claim to magnificence was an exquisite old shawl that had belonged to her aunt, rose-coloured silk, heavily fringed and embroidered, and for a while she had believed that she looked stylish until she arrived inside the Club.

'Don't worry!' Rob reached over and caught the tips of her fingers consolingly. 'You don't need diamonds, pet, or boutique dresses, just bare arms and bare shoulders and a young girl's beautiful breasts. You catch the eye just being yourself. Take that born-brunette blonde over there. I've never seen more diamonds at the one time in my life. I mean, she's just ablaze. It takes a few minutes to notice her gown is stretched to breaking point. If only middle-aged women would take a good fore and aft look at themselves they'd all go on a diet.'

'Surely the same goes for middle-aged men?' Amanda said dryly.

'True!' Rob looked around him, seeing the statement to be self-evident. 'One thing is certain, I'll always look after myself. It's absolutely bad, over-eating and drinking and no exercise. One must be faithful to a healthy régime.'

'Well, I'm trying!' she said.

'Serious matters aside, what about dancing? I can't resist the temptation to take you in my arms.'

'As long as you obey the rules, I'd love to!'

It was heaven just to be able to relax and Rob was a beautiful dancer, his slim compact body moving with an athlete's lithe co-ordination. Amanda didn't have to pretend she wasn't enjoying herself and she held her own easily upon a dance floor. After a while other couples began to get up and the group settled into a more gentle beat, a dreamy popular love song.

Amanda could feel the heat off Rob's smooth golden skin, the very faint tremble in his body.

'I could become addicted to you, Mandy!' he whispered against her cheek. 'You make me feel weak with desire. Your skin is like satin!'

'That's what's so good about being nineteen!'

'For God's sake!' He held her away a little, looking into her mocking green eyes. 'Aren't you ever going to be serious? I can't recall a cooler girl, and I've had dozens falling at my feet.'

'*I* see!'

'No, you don't!' He drew her back into his arms, holding her tightly. 'I know damned well I could easily fall in love with you.'

'Then you *would* have a problem!' she smiled.

'I can see that!' he returned a little waspishly, 'but let me tell you I won't give up. As a matter of fact, I'll find you a few books to read—educational stuff. I'd say you were suffering from repression. You're afraid to let go.'

'I enjoy myself in my own quiet way, though I get your direction.'

His hand slid caressingly over her back. 'Allowing yourself to be made love to isn't immoral. You've inherited an outdated set of values.'

'I can't accept that,' she said lightly. 'The rules are for our own protection.'

'My God!' Rob drew back a little to stare down at her. Her flawless skin was faintly flushed and the soft, full mouth was made for love. 'All right, I have a question. Just a small point I was wondering about. Could you ever fall in love with a married man?'

'Why bother?' she shrugged, though her heart lunged. 'Isn't an ordinary romance complicated enough without begging for unpleasantness?'

'You don't know the first thing about anything, do you? What about a man like, say, Marc Chandler? Strong meat for a mere girl, I agree, but I happen to notice he churned you up.'

'You didn't exactly act yourself either!' Amanda challenged him.

'True, but that's an entirely different kettle of fish. Would you like him to hurt you? He's a very sexy man. Add to that tons of money and a lot of class and....'

'....you still have a married man.'

'A lot of women make do with someone else's man.'

'You're beginning to annoy me,' she said coldly, and her luminous eyes flashed a deeper green.

'Why, pet? Surely I've missed something. Don't you think he's exciting?'

'If I thought that, I'd be a perfect fool. Actually he's almost a stranger to me, a naturally formidable man. Certainly he makes me feel very wary.'

'Then why let him drive you home? For one thing he had to go right out of his way.'

Amanda realised right then that she wasn't going to tell Rob anything. There was plenty of time for that; she had to speak to Doctor McGilvray first. She needed someone to advise her. Not Rob, who was watching her so closely, a hard expression in his changing hazel eyes.

'Speak of the devil!' he murmured, looking past her head. 'Guess who's just been ushered through the front door to a fanfare. Everyone seems to be spinning around him. Anyone else would look foolish, but he doesn't. The stunning Caro is by his side, even thinner than the last time I saw her. What does he do? Beat her? She's got an exquisite bauble around her throat, but she doesn't look in the least lighthearted. What's happening there, I wonder? You'd think life would be blissful, but maybe he frightens her as well. He has a reputation for ruthlessness. Maybe he bought her and decided he didn't want her?'

Amanda felt herself quivering and they came to a halt. 'You haven't been in Chandler long enough to know everyone's background. Mrs Chandler was a Langland before her marriage, and the Langland fortune compares quite favourably with the Chandlers'.

Old Mr Douglas Langland is still on the Board of Directors at the mine. He was a great friend of Marc's grandfather.'

'Really? *Marc?*'

'Mr Chandler. Let's sit down.' She moved in front of Rob back to the table where he stopped and held her chair.

'Don't lose your cool, sweetie!'

'I thought you were hoping I would, as quickly as possible.'

He sat down again opposite her and laughed. 'Just teasing, darling. I realise I was talking nonsense. Care to eat now?'

Amanda nodded, feeling as if all the brilliant lights in the room had dimmed. The Chandler party had been shown to their table and most eyes were temporarily fixed on them, including Rob's. Her own she kept on the single perfect red rose on the table. It was probable that she would have an opportunity to observe the beautiful Mrs Chandler later in the evening, and without blatant staring. Surely Marc Chandler would have seen *them*. He was the sort of man who missed nothing, and today she had as good as told him she had no personal interest in Rob. Not that it was his affair in any way. The wine waiter arrived with a bottle and after that, the first course.

Everything was very flavoursome and beautifully presented, but Amanda didn't share Rob's cheerful appetite. For a very fit young man he seemed to eat an incredible lot out of what appeared to be sheer necessity, but then perhaps he relaxed his régime at the weekend. It took a full half hour before she allowed her gaze to slide towards the Chandlers' table. A party of eight, and they all looked spectacularly prosperous. Marc Chandler had his sculptured head with its thick black waves turned towards the woman by his side. Whatever he was saying she was laughing, with a wonderful sparkle in her face— and it wasn't his wife.

Mrs Caroline Chandler was staring straight ahead of her, her light-coloured eyes dazzling with her jet black hair. She was, as Rob had pointed out, excessively slim, but she was still, Amanda thought, the most beautiful woman she had ever seen. Her black crêpe chiffon dress was splashed with bright flowers, but there was no life or vivacity in that perfect face. She might have been a statue of the Snow Queen with shining lifeless eyes.

Amanda's soft heart smote her and she found herself murmuring a prayer. How could a woman with everything in life look so frozen? She continued to watch the older woman with hidden anxiety. Did Mrs Chandler show her feelings to her husband and child? The eyes were a very light blue, almost transparent, the bone structure was very fine, a fraction sharp with too great a weight loss, the skin was very white and matt as if it never felt the sun.

'I think she's heading for a breakdown, or she's had it,' Rob said quietly. 'She looks utterly passionless, doesn't she? Perfect but passionless. A strange choice of wife for a man like that!'

'Perhaps she's ill ... unhappy?' Amanda said vaguely.

'The kid has these sudden temper tantrums,' Rob told her. 'I believe they last for quite a while. Perhaps there's some basic instability in the family. Obviously not on the father's side. Maybe he's cruel to her. He's a splendid-looking devil and he must call the tune.'

Silently Amanda finished her wine. It tasted bitter, as if there had been a change in its alchemy. Suddenly she wanted to go home, as though the other woman's locked-in melancholy affected her, but she knew Rob was enjoying himself. They danced only once more, but no one at the Chandler table appeared to notice them. She recognised the Hugh Elliots and Marc Chandler's uncle, Clive Chandler and his wife, but the rest of the party were unknown to her. It was only in the moment they were leaving that Amanda met Marc Chandler's dark eyes, glowing like coals against his darkly tanned skin. They slid over her from her head to her feet, though the glance only lasted a second, then he turned away with characteristic arrogance.

It was strange to feel burning in the fresh night air. The breeze blew in from the lake and Rob drew her against his shoulder. 'I enjoyed that.'

'So did I.' She tried to inject warmth into her voice, but somehow she struck a wrong note.

'Don't let those wretched Chandlers upset you. We live in a vastly different world. I must say the last time I saw the beauteous Caro she was in a vastly different mood. Could be she's on drugs.'

'As you say, let's forget about them!' Amanda looked up at the brilliant stars and not back at the Club. The grass had a velvet spring beneath her thin sandals and they walked across to the car in silence.

Before he turned the engine on, Rob pulled her to him almost roughly. 'Kiss me, darling. God knows I can't wait a moment longer!' He shuddered as he lowered his mouth, finding hers unerringly, exploring the curves of her lips, trying to force her mouth open.

'Please, Rob!' She wasn't ready for such a passionate embrace.

'Give a little, baby!' he groaned. 'I want you. Don't you understand how I feel?' He seemed to be crushing her, bruising her mouth. He was very much stronger and his hand moved from her shoulder to the curve of her breast, hungry for its tender promise.

Amanda hated him and she hated herself for not being able to break free. It wasn't the moment for anyone to walk towards the car, but a hard, cold voice brought them both back to reason.

'I beg your pardon, but you forgot something, Amanda.'

She drew back in nervous shock, her long ash-gold hair caught under Rob's hand. 'Mr Chandler!' She sounded dazed, disorientated, and Marc Chandler passed the rose silk shawl through the open car window.

'The waiter noticed it immediately, but of course he didn't know Courtney's car, so I offered to bring it. It *is* yours, isn't it?'

'I can't think how I came away without it. It must have slipped to the floor.'

'No doubt your mind was on other things!'

He made it sound as if she was a disgusting little girl, and anger welled up in her. 'That's usually the explanation isn't it? Thank you, Mr Chandler. I would have hated to lose it, it belonged to my aunt.'

'Goodnight, then!' He half lifted a hand, a tall, very arrogant man with cold black eyes.

Rob switched on the ignition and drew in his breath. 'What did he expect us to make, a full confession? Who the devil does he think he is anyway? Maybe he lusts after you himself.'

Amanda turned scarlet in the darkness. 'You should take more care with what you say, Rob.'

'I'm sorry, darling!' He reached out for her hand in quick contrition. 'And listen—I'm sorry if I offended you in any way. I'm going too fast with you, but I don't seem to be able to help it. You have a powerful effect on me.'

'I don't like being kissed with ferocity.'

'I'm sorry!' Rob said again. 'I'll be very tender and respectful from now on. Say you forgive me?'

'The only way I can forgive you, Rob, is if you don't act that way again. I like you, I've enjoyed this evening, but I'm very sensitive about how I'm treated and regarded.'

'But I hold you in the utmost respect, pet!' He looked at her and his hazel eyes were serious. 'It's that damned Chandler who's made you over-react. A black villain if ever there was one, yet he made it seem like a disgrace to kiss a girl, something illegal. Maybe he thought we had no right to do such a thing in the Club grounds.'

Amanda looked away, afraid to make a comment. Marc Chandler's attitude had upset her. Her hands were trembling and she could feel the heat all over her skin. He would have seen the way Rob was kissing her, of course, his hand at her breast, but did that give him the right to look so harsh and disapproving? Probably he would now consider her an unsuitable companion for his precious child. Good! Let him think she was wicked!

Cars flashed past them, their headlights blazing. It was late, but there was still plenty of traffic around.

The stars thickly threaded the black dome of the sky and the air was heavily scented with lemon from the elegant little myrtles that grew in dense numbers. Rob's face in the light from the dashboard was unusually serious as though he too felt his evening was spoiled.

'Almost there!' he said, certain now that she wasn't going to suggest he come in.

Amanda looked up quickly. 'Thank you for a lovely evening,' she said gravely,' and I did enjoy it right up until the clinch. It was pretty far gone for a first date.'

'It won't happen again, love,' he promised, prey to unusual feelings. God knows other girls thought little of their safety or reputation. 'I think it's going to rain tomorrow,' he added soberly. 'I don't suppose you'd care to take a run up to Mundoora for the Arts and Crafts Festival? The pottery and the leather work is always very good.'

'I'd love to,' said Amanda in a happier kind of voice.

'That's it, then. Shall I pick you up about two?'

'Lovely!' She didn't hesitate.

Rob drew up at the front gate and purposely left the engine running to reassure her. 'Naughty boys aren't allowed in, I suppose?'

'Not even good ones.'

'If there *are* any!' He moved imperceptibly and kissed her cheek. 'Take care, pretty one. I'll wait here until I see the lights. The old biddy next door is peering out in any case.'

'Mrs Farrell?' Amanda laughed beneath her breath. 'She's a pet really. A good friend.'

'It's easy to take a great liking to you, dear. Don't all the patients love you?'

'And I love them in return.'

'Yes, you do, you funny little thing. You have a very soft heart.'

'Until tomorrow, then!' She slipped away from him and he kept looking after her, a slender graceful girl moving like a dryad.

After a few moments the lights streamed out from the hall and front verandah and he could see her disturbingly feminine outline at the front door. She was waving, and it gave him a tremendous burst of hope. Such a charming frightened little virgin!

Amanda was early to the Medical Centre on Monday morning, half decided she was going to refuse Marc Chandler's offer. It was much better not to get involved in such an unhappy situation, and she did want a word with Doctor McGilvray.

The doctor was already there when she arrived. He greeted her pleasantly, his blue eyes approving her immaculate young appearance, then he turned and led her into his office.

'Enjoy your weekend? Do sit down, dear.'

'Thank you.' Amanda slid into the seat facing the big desk. 'I can't say I did really.' Her voice was a little shaky. 'I've been too worried about this job Mr Chandler has offered me. He's discussed it with you?'

'Yes.' The doctor sat down himself, rather heavily. 'You must admit the man has a problem.'

Amanda nodded dully. 'The thing is I don't think I can help him.'

'There's that!' The doctor slowly turned in his seat, fixing his eyes on a chart. 'You're so—so young!'

'Besides, I like my job here.'

'Indeed yes! Who's going run everything when you go? You've been a great help to me, Amanda, the way you look after things. Everybody likes you. You're very good with people, which is why perhaps you should give this thing a go. The child could only benefit from your help and guidance.' The chair swivelled back and he glanced at her face. 'What particular aspect is worrying you?'

'*Mrs* Chandler, I should think. She hasn't been given an opportunity to see me or interview me. She may have very different ideas about who should take charge of her child. It's quite a responsibility!'

'You go carrying my highest recommendation. Don't forget I'm Mrs Chandler's doctor and the child's. I think there's a real chance you may be able to help young Karin.'

'All I've heard is that she's delicate and she has temper tantrums,' sighed Amanda.

The doctor looked across at her sharply. 'That little girl is in the middle of a battlefield. It's our job, yours and mine, to do all we can for her. I know she's a privileged child in one sense of the word, but the temper tantrums may well be a simple cry for attention. Remember I'm speaking to you in the strictest confidence whether you take the job or not. Caroline Chandler has never been the same since the child was born. It wasn't a difficult birth—I should know, I was there. But the story has been put about that it nearly killed her. That wasn't the case at all. She simply doesn't want to have any more. She's a strange girl, very highly strung, like her mother before her.'

'Even so——' Amanda offered vaguely.

'The true victim is the child. Her father *must* be

away for so much of the time. Old Mrs Chandler tries to look after her and protect her. She doesn't enjoy the strained relationship she has with her daughter-in-law. It must be pretty exhausting when you're well into your sixties, though Elizabeth is fitter and more active than most.'

'You don't think there's a chance Mrs Caroline Chandler may refuse to have me in the house?'

The doctor hesitated, then said evenly, 'I should think Marc Chandler is as much the boss in his home as he is everywhere else. Caroline too, is to be pitied. Having a difficult temperament is like being in a cage. Her moods see-saw. One day she'll talk away quite happily for a long time, the next time I see her she's unwilling to even look at me. I suppose I don't take all that much notice. I see a lot of behavioural patterns.'

'There's another child too, a little boy. Karin's cousin.'

'Young Pip?' The doctor's memory came to his rescue. 'Nothing wrong with that boy. You won't have any trouble there. I mean to say, he does get sick from time to time, he has a mild bronchial allergy, but I can attend to that. At least I can put your mind at rest about the boy. He's a fine little chap, well adjusted and well mannered. Karin has been thoroughly indulged by her mother when she isn't being totally ignored. As you can imagine, this is very unsettling for a child.'

'I should think so!' said Amanda, remembering that shining stationary glance. 'I was half determined to say no.'

'You still can, my dear. No one is trying to argue you into it and certainly I don't want to see you get wounded yourself. On the one hand you have many qualities of particular value to the situation. On the other, you're little more than a child yourself, for all your instinctive good sense. As you say, it's a position of responsibility. In the normal family set-up I could have send you off straight away or at least within a couple of days so you could train someone else, but I must warn you, as no doubt Marc has warned you himself, that his wife is completely hopeless at taking charge of her own child. It's a bit odd and I find it inexcusable. Perhaps if she wasn't living such a life of luxury....' The old doctor broke off uncomfortably.

'Do you think I could do it?' Amanda asked earnestly.

'Would I say so if I thought you couldn't?' There was a pause while the doctor stared into her face. 'You've grown into a very beautiful girl, Amanda. So many things could have gone wrong, with your being orphaned so early, yet you've turned out beautifully, while others far more fortunate make a complete mess of their lives. If you don't take this job Marc Chandler simply has to find someone else.'

'Why does he want *me*, at all?'

The doctor frowned, looking very serious. 'It's possible that being a man he likes the look of you. I know that sounds a little disquieting, but it's a point. Whatever you do we must think this all out. You're a clever girl and you're extraordinarily competent. He knows your background and if he didn't trust you, you wouldn't be allowed anywhere near the place.'

'I know what you mean,' she said dryly. 'I suppose the only way to find out if I can handle it or not is be taken on for a trial period.'

The doctor rubbed his chin and nodded without comment.

'He's going to ring me today. What shall I say?'

'You'll do it!' The doctor picked up a letter, glanced at it and then threw it into the wastepaper basket. 'Who on earth are we going to get to replace you?'

'Lots of people!' Amanda said with a sudden smile.

'A pity!' the doctor said briefly. 'You were entirely what we wanted.'

'I'll train someone, you'll see.'

'I don't like to think about it this morning,' the doctor said protestingly. 'Can you run the ad? Make it as short as you can.'

Amanda stood up and said seriously, 'I just want to thank you for being so kind to me over all these long years. I've enjoyed working at the Centre, and I know I've learnt a lot.'

The doctor stood up and came round the desk, putting his hand on her shoulder. 'I know you have, and you're gentle with suffering. Remember that. And, Amanda, feel free to speak to me at any time about anything that's troubling you. I usually call in at the house once a fortnight or whenever I'm needed. Don't let the young Mrs Chandler rattle you. You're there for the child.'

'And I want to help her if I can.'

It was late afternoon before Marc Chandler rang, his voice very businesslike and rather cold. 'Tell me, Amanda, have you decided?'

'I have!' she said a little tensely, affected by his tone. 'I'd very much like to help Karin if I could. I thought

I'd suggest a trial period of employment.'

'Anything you say. At least that's one thing off my mind.'

There was a long silence as though he was already thinking of something else. 'When would you like me to start?' she asked doubtfully.

'Just a moment, Amanda.' His voice came back to her, clearly preoccupied, and she heard the murmur of another voice in the background. She swallowed on the little lump in her throat and waited, then he said: '*Now*....' in so crisp a tone she could almost see the brilliant flash of his eyes. 'I'm telling *you*, then you can put me through to McGilvray, I've found a possible replacement for you if the Doc gives the O.K. Her name is Rae Walker and she's been working here in the office since she left school.'

'I know her!' Amanda said with a quick ripple of gratitude. 'I think she'd take my place quite easily.'

'Quite.' He sounded a little impatient. 'If you could arrange it, I'd like to take you up to the house to-night. My mother would like to meet you.'

'But isn't it all decided?' Amanda asked, her throat dry. She had seen Mrs Elizabeth Chandler many many times in the course of her short life and been thoroughly impressed.

'Of course!' he agreed with weary bitterness. 'And isn't it a good thing! It doesn't pay to have only half one's mind on the job when one's dealing with men and lives. Whatever you're thinking, Amanda, you're wanted and needed at the house. I have no more time to reassure you. You're a sensible girl, so for God's sake, act it. I'll pick you up at what time?'

'Any time you say. I'm quite free.'

'I certainly hope so!' It came out like a warning shot. 'What about after surgery? Mrs Lindal takes over at six, doesn't she?'

'Yes,' Amanda offered quietly.

'Then six it is. You may as well have dinner with us.'

Amanda silently shook her blonde head in protest, but she was committed now. 'Will I be seeing Karin?' she asked.

'Yes. I won't say for long. Now put me through to McGilvray, like a good girl. It's a bit difficult trying to fit everyone in.'

'I'll connect you now!' It was purely a personal reaction, but he made her hands shake. She gazed at them thoughtfully for perhaps a full minute. What had she let herself in for?

CHAPTER THREE

AMANDA was still shaking when they arrived at the Chandler mansion that evening. She had found the time to wash her face and carefully re-apply a light make-up, but her dress was the same one she had started the day in: fine white cotton, almost, but not quite, a uniform. It seemed excessively ordinary in such a setting as the Big House, which was the way the townspeople always referred to the main Chandler residence.

A Chinese manservant showed them in, bowing not obsequiously as some might have done, but with natural dignity. Mrs Elizabeth Chandler was waiting for them in the drawing room. Amanda truly didn't see anything in particular, though she was uncomfortably conscious of a life style very far removed from her own. There were antiques, paintings, sculptures, objets d'art. There was still plenty of summer light, so no chandeliers blossomed above them, but there were flowers blooming everywhere, lovely arrangements that lent a calming, welcoming touch.

'Are you nervous?' Marc Chandler looked down at her shining blonde head.

'Yes,' she said truthfully.

'How terrible to be young!' he said ruefully.

'I don't think you could ever have been nervous even as a child.'

Unexpectedly he laughed and it completely dissolved

the autocratic, faintly forbidding mask. 'You're very forthright for a governess.'

'Then I must apologise.'

'Don't!' he said curtly. 'It always irritates me—apologies.'

'But then I don't know you well.'

'You don't know me at all!' he rebuked her.

And I'm not really sure I want to! Amanda's thoughts were rebellious, but he was looking down at her as though he could scarcely care less.

They were half way across the beautifully proportioned entrance hall when there was commotion above the stairs.

'Let me *go*!'

It was a child's voice, sharp and defiant. Marc Chandler threw his dark head up, a flash of black anger in his expression, then the next second a small girl about eight raced down the divided stairway, her shoes making a racket on the terrazzo floor. 'Daddy!'

'Weren't you told to stay upstairs?'

'Why?' The child came to a halt beside Amanda, staring her up and down with the sharp intelligence of an inquisitive monkey.

'Oh, I'm *so* sorry, Mr Chandler!' A motherly, middle-aged woman followed the child down the stairs, blinking nervously. 'She simply got away from me.'

'All right!' he said briefly. 'Forget it. Now that you're here, Karin, you may say good evening to Miss Raymond. She's here to be a friend to you and bring you up to date with your lessons.'

Karin's radiant blue eyes looked up alertly. 'But she could be a wicked person who hates me. Mummy says there's no one we can trust. Besides, you know how I loathe blonde hair!'

Amanda's face broke into an understanding, wry smile. 'I assure you it's natural, Karin, and I'm really not so bad when you get to know me. How are you this evening?'

'Oh, so-so!' the child moaned.

'God in Heaven!' Marc Chandler said under his breath, studying his daughter's exquisite little face as though it discouraged him. 'Having seen Miss Raymond and ventured your stricken opinion, perhaps you'll now go upstairs with Brenda.'

For an instant Karin looked as if she was suffering unspeakable anguish, then she burst out with venom, 'You'll see! Little kids have got something to say for themselves. I don't have to have any wacky old governess if I don't want to. I can get an education any time I like. I only have to go into the library.'

'That will do!' her father said coldly. 'You've told your story, now you may say goodnight.'

Karin looked vengefully at Amanda, her light eyes brilliant. 'Mummy doesn't like blonde hair either. You'll see!'

'Then I daresay you are the only two in the world who don't!'

'Oh, please, Mr Chandler!' Amanda was bothered by his grim tone and the effect it was having on the child. 'Karin and I have only just met. We need a little time to get to know one another.'

'I've got a feeling we're not going to!' Karin flared shrilly, blinking back tears. 'No matter what anyone says I'm not going to have any cruel governess in the house!'

'Terrible and bad as it is, you're going to!' Her father regarded her thoughtfully for a moment, then he scooped her up under one arm, carrying her back up the stairs with the unfortunate Brenda scurrying up after them. Amanda expected to hear cries of outrage or a single wail, but there was complete silence, then the soft thud of a door closing.

'Oh dear!' she said aloud, then realised she was being observed.

'I see you've met Karin.' A tall, distinguished-looking woman walked towards her, holding out a spare, elegant hand. 'How do you do, my dear. I'm Elizabeth Chandler, Marc's mother—Karin's grandmother, and a very harassed one at times!'

Amanda returned the pleasant smile and shook Mrs Chandler's hand gently. 'I'm sorry, but I seem to have made a bad start.'

'Not at all, my dear! Karin was positively *dying* to meet you. She just has this terrible way of expressing herself. Come into the drawing room so we can make ourselves comfortable.'

She turned and led the way and Amanda had time to admire the tall, erect figure, the straight back and narrow waist, the crisp silvery-grey waves that went so strikingly with the still, jet black eyes and brows. At nearly seventy Mrs Elizabeth Chandler could still be described as a fine-looking woman and she didn't in the least make Amanda feel awkward or less than suitably dressed for such an interview.

'How good it is to meet you!' She sat down and patted the sofa beside her. 'Do come and sit beside me, my dear. Please don't be disturbed by Karin's reference to your hair. We had an accident to her

favourite doll, a few months back. She's never forgotten and Francesca, that was the doll's name—Marc
brought her back from overseas—had impossibly
beautiful long golden locks. It's a sad story. No doubt
Karin will confide in you when she knows you better.'

Amanda took her seat on the sofa, one of a pair
that flanked the magnificent white marble fireplace.
'That makes me feel a little better, though of course
I'm sorry to hear about Francesca. I had my favourite
doll, too, when I was a little girl.'

'She has plenty of others, as you might imagine,'
Elizabeth Chandler smoothed down her dark blue
skirt, 'but Francesa was just so beautiful and her father
gave it to her. Poor little Karin, she called us all so
many names I felt quite ashamed, and I'd done absolutely nothing. But enough of that. Doctor McGilvray
speaks very highly of your capabilities, Amanda,
though it *was* Marc who first thought of you. Thank
goodness he did! I can see at a glance that you're a
sensible, sensitive girl and we can trust you. You see,
my dear, being a Chandler in this town is almost like
living in a goldfish bowl. People always have to have
something to talk about, I know, but they seem to
ignore all the good things and concentrate on spreading
a lot of gossip that most people believe. The wilder and
sillier the story the better!'

Amanda looked at her quickly and saw the distress
in her face. 'Don't upset yourself, Mrs Chandler. Nothing that happens in this house will ever be passed on
by me as gossip. I owe loyalty to my employer, always
supposing Karin wants me. I'm a little worried about
that.'

For a second Mrs Chandler looked aghast, looking

fully into Amanda's clear eyes. 'Please, dear, haven't I been just telling you how glad I am you've come? Very few girls would have suited, you know, especially in this house. Quite frankly I need your help with my grandchild. Marc is just so desperately pressured with business the job of rearing Karin has fallen largely to me. At the same time I haven't got full control of the child. My daughter-in-law Caroline is just too unwell for most of the time and Karin can't go to her with her little problems. I worry about Caroline quite as much as I worry about my granddaughter. On the days Caroline is exhausted Karin seems bent on mischief. In fact, because I try to keep the house quiet the child gets away with murder. Then when Caroline feels so much better she tries to make it up to her little daughter with perhaps too much indulgence. It isn't good for the child. I'm afraid too I'm not as young as I was and it's beginning to tell. Much as I love her, I must admit Karin is a little bit of a problem and if I try to correct her Caroline flies into a fury. It's amazingly wearing. I never had to lift a hand to any one of my children. My husband was a strict disciplinarian and Marc particularly was trained to take over a huge responsibility. Now one small girl seems to be defeating me, and there's so much that's good and sweet in her.'

'She's certainly a lovely looking child,' Amanda agreed. 'But if you as her grandmother have trouble disciplining Karin when she needs it mightn't I be entirely unsuccessful, Mrs Chandler? Karin's mother wouldn't take kindly to interference from me. I'm not sure I could manage unless I had a free hand. I hope I shall be understanding to Karin, but I can't allow her to defy me, especially as I have to bring her school work up to date.'

For a second Mrs Chandler hesitated, one hand to the fine single strand of pearls at her throat. 'Caroline knows you have a job to do—Marc has spoken to her. The other thing is, we've set aside the east wing of the house for your use, yours and the children's. Marc's told you about Philip?'

'Yes, he has.'

'And you've nothing to bother you there. Pip is a dear little chap. You'll get on well.'

Amanda let her eyes linger on the lovely arrangement of yellow roses on the long low table between the two sofas. 'Would I be expected to teach Philip as well?'

'Not at all, unless he wants to join the lessons as a bit of fun or to keep him occupied. He's a very bright little boy and he's almost finished his first year at school. I believe they break up at the end of next week. It's a private school, so they finish a little earlier than the other children. He'll be joining us then. Jennifer and Ross leave the next day. It's a study trip really, mixed in with a little pleasure. Jennifer has been very good staying home with Pip all the time. Now we feel he's old enough not to miss her too much, and she does need the break. By the way, they're coming over to dinner this evening just to say hello.'

And to look me over, Amanda instinctively knew. She couldn't help herself as she glanced down at her dress. 'Had I known Mr Chandler was going to include me for dinner and to invite me to the house to meet you I would have worn something less clinical,' she apologised.

'One would hardly notice, dear. You have a natural elegance—please don't feel uncomfortable on that score. Anyway, Jennifer knows you've come straight from the Centre. Actually she placed you immediately.' The fine dark eyes looked beyond Amanda's pure, young profile. 'Oh, there you are, darling!'

Amanda swung her head just as Marc Chandler walked across the glowing parquet floor with richly woven scatter rugs to define the conversation areas. 'You may take it Karin has quietened!' he said briefly.

His mother didn't smile. 'You didn't smack her, did you, darling?'

'I did.' Standing there he didn't look a kind man but a man of ruthless decision. 'Don't worry, Mamma, we parted good friends. Brenda will look after her, though it looks as if the job's killing her. How's everything here?'

Elizabeth Chandler dropped her eyes from her son's and smiled at Amanda. 'Your choice as always, darling, is impeccable.'

'Really?' For a moment the handsome mouth looked bitter and sullen. 'I'm sure you can see, Amanda, that the job won't be easy.'

'I'll do my very best as long as I'm given full control of Karin during our working hours.'

'I see!' He drew in his breath and looked down at her. 'Anything else?'

'I don't think so. I'm very glad Mrs Chandler approves of me.'

'The one you've seen!'

'Really, Marc!' His mother found her voice. 'I've assured Amanda you've spoken to Caroline and she understands perfectly that Amanda must have a free hand if she's to take charge of Karin and bring her up to date with her lessons. All these little illnesses have held her back, but if she takes an intelligent interest in her work she'll pick up in no time.'

'Ah!' her son said.

'You're in a strange mood, darling!'

'I'm tired!' he said a little flatly. 'When did Caro go out?'

'Straight after lunch. She didn't really say if she'd be back for dinner or not. But no problem, there's always plenty of everything. I was telling Amanda Jenny and Ross will be here.'

'Don't die of embarrassment, Amanda,' Marc Chandler said rather cruelly. 'You look wonderful!'

'Should you not have a drink to relax, dear?' his mother suggested, her whole demeanour one of loving concern.

'I could use it!' he said briefly. 'But first I'll show Amanda the east wing. You and the children will be together and you'll have plenty of privacy. There's even a room overlooking the rose walk that we've turned into a schoolroom. You'll have complete authority to throw your weight around.'

'I hope there's no need!' Amanda returned a shade crisply, and Elizabeth Chandler threw her a swift look of approval.

'Go with Marc, dear. I feel so much better now that I've met you. And listen, Amanda, you have a firm ally in me.'

'Then I accept the challenge!'

'Good girl!'

'Good *brave* girl!' Marc Chandler seconded dryly. 'Come along, Amanda, and I'll take you on a tour of your domain.'

Amanda smiled at Mrs Chandler and stood up. 'I must admit I've never been in such a beautiful house before. I'm privileged to live in it for the term of my employment.'

'*We* love it!' Mrs Chandler agreed. 'Once it was a magic kingdom for me when I first married. My family were considered well off, but we never had what the Chandlers had—the antiques, the glories of the past, the fine collection of paintings, all so beautifully housed. One needs a very large house, of course, a feeling of space, the high ceilings and the architectural details that contribute so much to displaying one's loved and treasured possessions. There are many things I can show you when we have time.'

'You wouldn't be interested in the bills for its maintenance?' Marc Chandler gave Amanda a sardonic glance.

'I imagine they're enormous!' she commented.

'I don't pay too much attention. Only now and again. Excuse us, Mamma, won't you?'

'Of course, dear. Amanda may have some suggestions of her own to make things easier for her. You'll tell us, won't you, Amanda?'

'If that's what you want, Mrs Chandler.'

'I do, dear!' The dark eyes so like yet so unlike her son's met Amanda's directly. 'If we make you comfortable and reasonably happy you'll stay, and I want you to stay!'

'Thank you, and I want to help!'

'Heart-warming!' Marc Chandler agreed. 'When's Jen arriving?'

'About seven.'

'Then come along, Amanda.' He took her elbow firmly and propelled her across the large room. 'Perhaps you won't find this unbridled opulence upstairs, but I think you'll be comfortable.'

Amanda shivered, though the breeze that blew in through the jalousied French doors carried all the warm, fragrant scents of the garden. She would have to constantly renew her vitality to keep up with Marc Chandler, but at least something warmed her as she walked with the tall, dark man at her side: Mrs Elizabeth Chandler approved of her, and that meant a lot.

From under her fringe of dark lashes she had a jumbled recollection of impressively scaled rooms, richly and harmoniously decorated, the Y-shaped stairway with gleaming mahogany balusters, the long corridor, its monotony broken by cherished paintings and open armchairs set at intervals, then Marc Chandler paused and opened one of the heavy panelled doors.

'Your bedroom,' he said, and waited for her to precede him into the room. 'It has a connecting sitting room with Karin's room beyond. Pip we've put into the smaller bedroom to the left. I'll show it to you after we're through here.'

'But it's very grand!' Amanda crossed the wide expanse of carpet to gaze out the open window. 'I've never been made such a fuss of in my life!'

'You could be!' he said, and turned on the overhead chandelier, a charming fantasy of bronze and porcelain shaped like a bouquet of flowers. 'The traditional old fourposter bed to lose yourself in. A desk, seeing you're going to be working hard.'

'It's beautiful!' she breathed unequivocally. 'A bedroom on the grandscale. I'll find it very difficult settling back to my own.'

He half smiled, a cynical expression in his brilliant dark eyes. 'You're an honest child!' he commented.

'Why not?'

'No doubt time will take care of that. Women are full of guile.'

'Then I hope I'm always a poor hand at it!' She stared back at him, glad to see the hard, beautiful mouth relaxing. 'May I see Karin's room? Karin's new room, I take it?'

'We've shifted most of her treasures in. Brenda usually keeps an eye on her during the night. She's devoted to the family and she's been with us for years, but her duties are more properly connected with the household. Anyway, she has a heart condition and Karin is too much for her!'

He was standing in the doorway of the adjoining room and Amanda had to pass him. She fixed her eyes on the small circular table beyond, her head slightly reeling. There was something about Marc Chandler, a latent sensuality she didn't want to know about, but she was already aware in her heart that she felt the strong pull of it.

She moved her attention over the deep comfortable seating of the armchairs, the graceful upright lines of the small chairs around the table. Indoor plants bloomed luxuriantly in their sheltered light-filled position and there was a wall of books and objets d'art in

separate niches. 'We could have our meals here sometimes.'

'You could. I'm quite sure you'll want to!'

She hesitated nervously, then glanced out of the
window overlooking the rose garden. The brief
lavender twilight was almost gone, but she could see
the roses' heads nodding in the breeze, masses and
masses of them in a staggering variety of colours,
through the pinks to the crimsons, the palest cream to
the deep apricot, the pure, virginal white. Their scent
carried far and wide and she caught a glimpse of a
white cast-iron lace gazebo overgrown with ivy, jasmine
and the lemon banksia rose, China Spring.

'Come along, Amanda!' She felt Marc's hand heavy
on her shoulder. 'You'll have plenty of time to look
out at the roses.'

His touch shook her badly, though he seemed un-
aware of her nervous recoil. She went with him to
Karin's room, which wasn't as big as her own and
furnished in a lighter, airier fashion with filmy drapes
and a blue and white bedspread. A day bed stood in one
corner of the room covered in the same fresh blue and
white pattern and the ivory walls complemented the
dark polished floor with its big circular white rug,
heavily fringed. An antique open-shelved cabinet
housed a collection of very expensive-looking dolls
and Amanda knew that at least two of them, waxen-
faced with large melting brown eyes, belonged to the
Victorian period. It was the perfect retreat for a rich
and pampered little girl.

'You'll all have to share a bathroom directly across
the corridor, but I don't imagine that will be any real
problem. No suggestions so far?'

'Not a one.'

'Then we'll look at Pip's room and the schoolroom.' He walked ahead of her switching on lights as he went, his dark, rugged profile etched in pure gold. 'This has always been the guest wing, so there were very few changes to make beyond changing the curtains and things in Karin's room. My mother attended to all that.'

'When shall I be meeting Mrs Chandler, Karin's mother?'

'My wife?' He swung on her, forcing her to stand still, and she flung up a hand in near-fright. She looked very light and delicate against the panelled door, her green eyes deepening with an onrush of turbulent feelings. Why did he try to make a fool of her, this man?

'It's a little difficult with two Mrs Chandlers. Unless I say Senior and Junior!'

'Then let's get it settled. Because there *are* two!'

Her blonde head came up and colour flooded her cheeks. 'You chose me for this position, Mr Chandler, yet it's clear to me that you don't approve of me entirely.'

'On the contrary, I find you highly suitable in many ways.'

'Then why do you try to make a fool of me?'

The midnight glance leapt over her with ruthless detachment. 'I'm sorry if I gave you that impression. I'm not used to dealing with sensitive young girls.'

'You have a daughter,' she pointed out.

'Yes.' He turned away from her and his manner told her plainly that he was impatient to conclude their tour. Philip's room was a shade too overpowering for a small boy, but the room set aside for the schoolroom was ideal for the purpose, full of natural light, catching all the prevailing breezes and delightfully furnished with a mixture of scaled-down pieces of furniture and a highly functional long table with high-backed swivel chairs. A big black board in a frame had been fixed to one wall and there was a tall glass-fronted cabinet full of textbooks and exercise books of all kinds.

'We should be quite happy working here!' Amanda said.

'You've only to tell me if there's anything you need.'

'Thank you.' She half turned to smile at him and found his eyes on her, brilliant and brooding.

'No one could look less like a governess,' he commented suddenly.

'You should have thought of that in advance!' Somehow she found herself answering him back.

'At least my mother is strongly in favour of you.'

'Might it not be better if Karin and her mother were of that opinion?'

'I promise you neither of them will give you any trouble.'

This drew an ironic smile from Amanda. 'I do hope you're right. Sometimes first meetings set a pattern.'

There was a flicker of real humour in his brilliant black eyes. 'I know!' Deliberately he switched off the light and the room was cast into dusky shadows that robbed Amanda of confidence. 'Come along!' he said, with barely controlled patience.

Disturbed, she crossed the room to go out of the far door as though she was in a desperate race to get there before him. There was scarcely enough light left for her to find her way and the blood seemed to be beating meaninglessly in her veins. When she was almost past him she stumbled rather badly over a small camphor wood box she later found out was full of hundreds of pieces of Leggo. It was humiliating and almost like a rotten trick, so when he caught her shoulders to steady her she struggled wildly and broke away.

'You little fool!' The sardonic voice was full of contempt.

From her quiet, calm existence she seemed plunged into a whirlpool of seething emotions. 'Forgive me, I pulled away from you for quite a different reason.'

'I wonder. You acted afraid to me!' His voice was deep and even, but there was a kind of fury in it.

Amanda turned her head sharply so she was staring up into his eyes. 'I thought you were trying to make a fool of me.'

'Exactly how?'

'By allowing me to trip over that damned box!'

He frowned, the winged black eyebrows drawing together, then his mouth twitched in involuntary humour. 'Better a silly child than a fool woman! That box wasn't there this morning. I could easily have stumbled over it myself.'

'Then I accept your explanation.'

'That's very good of you!' He stared down at her with his habitual expression of dark arrogance. 'I'm a decade and more older than you, Amanda, a married man with a child—no target believe me for your puritanical disapproval!'

'I've never felt a flicker of it!' she lied.

'Really?' His voice sounded indifferent. 'One might imagine you struggle wildly when any man touches you, only I happen to know different.'

She moved then, reaching for the doorknob and opening the door.

'Don't bother to answer!' He caught her up easily, glancing down into her face.

'I don't think I need to, do I?' She was recovering quickly, though she was conscious that she was trembling in every limb.

'Not unless you get into serious trouble. You looked pretty much to me as if you were about to yell for help.'

His voice was hard and dry and Amanda had to fight to control her anger. '*You* panic me, Mr Chandler, far more than Rob Courtney ever could,' she snapped.

He took this without a flicker of changing expression. 'You may be absolutely certain not in the same way.'

Colour flooded her cheeks and she looked up at him, her eyes huge and intense. 'You know perfectly well what I mean.'

'I do. In fact I'm quite concerned for your welfare.'

'I wouldn't be in the least concerned!' she retorted quite heatedly for one of her gentle nature. 'I've been looking after myself for a long time.'

'You've never been exposed to risk in your life,' he returned bluntly.

'Is that what I look like?' Despite herself she had to ask.

'Yes.' His black eyes flicked her face again. 'A limpid-eyed little innocent, but I find it just right in a governess.'

They had come to the top of the divided stairway and Amanda drew a long, shaky breath. 'I just hope it's going to work out, Mr Chandler!'

'Surely you don't find the prospect too daunting?'

She looked up at him half despairingly as though she found his height and his determined aura, ominous. 'I'd like to succeed for Karin's sake.'

'Then that's all I ask. Let's go downstairs, Amanda. It's been a long day and I could do with a drink.'

She preceded him like a child, hugging the banister. Some instinct in her was clamouring to be heard while her mind was trying to bury it. Marc Chandler was the kind of man to leave a woman feeling lacerated, and all her sympathies were with his absent wife. Caroline Chandler was the real key to her remaining in this house.

During dinner, under Elizabeth Chandler's calming influence, Amanda found it easy to talk. It was a far more formal meal than anything she had ever been used to, nevertheless no one could discover any awkward shyness in her. She knew exactly how closely Jennifer and Ross Fullerton were listening and watching, but she had no need to worry. Whatever they saw and heard they visibly relaxed more and more with each course, grateful instead of anxious that Amanda would be looking after their precious only child.

Jennifer was very much like her brother without his shattering charisma and her husband Ross was really very nice and totally in love with his wife. It showed in his softening, tender expression every time he turned his head to look at her, and Amanda couldn't help comparing him with his brother-in-law. Both men were about the same age with a similar background, but where Amanda felt she could communicate with Ross Fullerton as a normal, pleasant human being, she couldn't help but go in considerable awe of Marc Chandler. His looks and manner hypnotised her against her will and she was especially conscious that while the Fullerton marriage was a very happy one, Marc

Chandler's was not. He was too cynical a man and he rarely smiled with his eyes and his mouth.

Coffee was served in the drawing room and Jennifer sat beside Amanda on one of the big sofas delicately balancing her coffee cup and filling Amanda in with all 'Pip's little quirks!' Her dark eyes, so much lighter and warmer than her brother's, danced with amused remembrances and Elizabeth Chandler looked across at them both with pleased eyes.

'Let me take your cup away from you, Amanda, you're finished. Would you like another?'

'No, thank you,' Amanda said gently. 'I don't usually drink a lot of coffee, but that was superb.'

'Even the price makes me nervous!' Ross Fullerton said suddenly in his pleasant well modulated voice. 'I seem to remember your parents, Amanda. Your mother was a blonde, like you?'

'Yes, she was. She was beautiful!'

'Who could doubt it?' he said gallantly. 'I know she would be very proud of you.'

'Thank you. I'd like to think so.'

'You're alone now, aren't you, my dear?' he asked her.

'Amanda's aunt died in March of this year,' Marc Chandler interposed. 'It can't be pleasant to be so young and so entirely alone.'

'Well, now we've met we can be friends,' Jennifer Fullerton said quietly, putting her empty cup down on the marble-topped table. 'I'd like you to come to dinner with us before we go. You could meet Pip and get to know him a little. Even if I say so myself he's a delightful child, though he does use his charm rather deliberately at times. Just like his Uncle Marc!'

'Come, come!' her brother chided gently, and for the first time Amanda saw the full power of his smile.

Ross gave a laugh and Jennifer cooed smilingly, 'Don't worry—you know I adore both of you!' She reached out and touched her brother's arm. 'It's wonderful to see you relaxed.'

'And am I?'

'More so than on our last visit!'

'We prefer not to talk about that, don't we, Mamma?' There was a flash of some turbulent expression in his eyes.

'Yes, darling. So don't. I'm enjoying this evening.'

'I've noticed that,' he answered. 'Amanda must have something to do with it.'

'Indeed she has!' Mrs Chandler smiled, and her smile showed the same warm friendliness as her daughter's. 'Being lovely to look at helps, but I'm sure Amanda is going to be a great help to me when you're all out of the house and I'm trying to cope.'

'I believe it comes naturally to her.' Marc Chandler looked across at Amanda, willing her effortlessly to lift her eyes to him.

'The only one who doesn't seem to be on my side is Karin!' she offered in all honesty.

Jennifer glanced at her mother for a moment. 'I take it Amanda has already met Karin?'

'For a few moments,' Elizabeth Chandler answered.

'And was it so dreadful?'

'Not at all,' Amanda returned frankly. 'Karin is only a little girl, after all.'

Jennifer lowered her eyes as though there was a lot she could say by way of a crash course on handling

Karin, but it was obviously not the right time. 'Karin will be just fine with the right person and she's very fond of Pip. Don't worry, Amanda, just act as if you're in charge and you know it.'

'All right, then!' Amanda smiled and her eyes dropped to her watch. 'I don't think I should stay any longer. You'll all want to talk privately, but it's been a very pleasant and helpful experience coming to dinner this evening. Thank you!'

'Such exquisite manners!' Marc Chandler drawled gently.

'Don't take any notice of him, Amanda!' Jennifer warned. 'He can't go for five minutes without teasing. It's a kind of game.'

Of which he is the master, Amanda thought.

Mrs Chandler stood up and held out her hand. 'When can you come to us, Amanda?'

'At the beginning of next week,' she said, and picked up her large shoulder bag. 'I have to be on hand for a few days to train the new receptionist. It will make things easier for her and the staff.'

'I understand,' Elizabeth Chandler nodded graciously. 'I want to thank you too, dear, for coming along tonight. You've put all our minds at rest!'

'By that Mamma means Ross and I can go away happy to leave Pip in your care,' said Jennifer, moving to her mother's side. Like all the Chandlers she had her own magnetism and her grooming was inevitably perfect and expensive. Still she smiled warmly as though she was anxious to have Amanda on her side. 'I'll ring you about coming to meet Pip, shall I? We can have a long talk!'

'I'd like that,' Amanda returned simply. She was either being very brave or very stupid committing herself to the Chandlers.

'And how are you getting home?' Ross Fullerton asked with smiling concern. 'You have a car?'

'Not on my present salary!' Amanda confessed.

'Then you'll be able to save as soon as you come to us,' Marc Chandler said smoothly. 'Now, perhaps, to smooth your way, I'll drive you home.'

'Thank you.' It was all she could say. No one in this area used public transport, if indeed there was a single bus ferrying along the river road.

They were all moving out towards the entrance hall when two people came at a wild, laughing rush through the great studded double front doors that stood open to the perfumed night air.

Jennifer, beside Amanda, came to an abrupt halt, looking almost fearfully at her brother's grim profile, while old Mrs Chandler's aristocratic face was filled with a mixture of distaste and regret. Amanda, however, was only vaguely aware of these impressions, for the young Mrs Chandler dominated her eye.

CHAPTER FOUR

TONIGHT the pale blue eyes glittered with an unnatural brilliance and the high, perfect cheekbones were hectic with colour.

'Hello, everybody!' Caroline cried gaily. 'If this were anywhere else, I'd think it was a welcoming party!'

'Oh, Caroline!' Jennifer exclaimed into the shocked hush.

'Oh, Caroline!' The young Mrs Chandler actually aped her sister-in-law's voice, then she laughed.

Rather chillingly, Amanda thought. She knew she was staring, but she couldn't credit the degree of change in Marc Chandler's wife. Surely there was a real malice twisting those sharp, perfect features? She remembered the equally strange calm of the woman at the Country Club—not that she could detect any calm in Mrs Caroline Chandler now. Then too, though she looked stunning, there was a certain carelessness in her grooming, for her long dark hair was falling over her neck and shoulders and her filmy jacaranda blue dress was something less than beautifully fresh. It was like looking at a blurred copy of a masterpiece and Amanda experienced an instant of shocked disappointment.

The man behind her everyone ignored altogether, as though they were blind to him.

'Don't delay, darling!' Caroline called to her husband almost frantically. 'Send Dom away!'

'I'll do better than that, I'll kill him!'

The man called Dom reacted instantly. 'I'll get a court order out to restrain you.'

'And I'll have the pleasure of breaking your neck first!'

Amanda couldn't help it. She gave a gasp and Elizabeth Chandler stepped forward swiftly and put her hand over her son's arm. 'Must you do this, Dominic? Don't you care for your cousin?'

The man Dominic's cheeks burned a hot red. 'I care more for her than your precious son!'

'Forgive me, but no one can believe that at all. Would you please go? This is my home and you'll never be welcome here.'

'Don't go away, Dom!' Caroline Chandler ordered sharply, turning so white Amanda thought she was about to fall.

'*Get out!*' Marc Chandler said in a voice that would have made an impression on stone.

'Say goodbye to me, Dom!' Caroline cried, and Amanda realised she was no longer in control of herself. 'I need you. We need each other!'

Marc Chandler was beside her so quickly she didn't realise his intention until he had scooped her up in his arms like a child. 'Let me *go!*' she screamed. 'I hate you!'

He drew her thin body higher and closer, starting to walk up the stairway. 'I hate you, Marc!' Caroline Chandler continued to struggle for a while, then gave up against such hard strength, seeming to dissolve against him. 'I hate you, Marc. I didn't think it was possible to hate anyone so much!'

'Then why don't you divorce me?'

Perhaps it was merciful her harsh wails were smothered up against his chest. They bothered Amanda dreadfully, so she was scarcely aware that the man Dominic's light eyes were upon her.

'And who's this golden-haired child?' he drawled.

'That doesn't matter to you!' Ross Fullerton returned sharply. 'You've been asked to go, so I suggest you do so. And while you're talking about court orders you can be prevented from coming to this house.'

'I thought Marc was at the mine!'

'Caroline just told you that,' Elizabeth Chandler said more quietly. 'She thrives on confrontation, as you know. Just as *I* know you fear my son!'

'With good reason!' said Jennifer, and gave a low, scornful laugh. 'Go away, Dom. Caroline doesn't really give a twopenny damn about you. She just uses you like she uses everyone else!'

'Jennifer!' Elizabeth Chandler turned to her daughter with a quick rush of words. 'Please don't say any more. It's all so....'

'Degrading?' Caroline's cousin gave a twisted sneer. 'Such a fine, respectable family, and Marc so rich and compelling with a wife who hates him.'

'Can you really believe that?' Elizabeth Chandler asked quietly. 'We all realise Caroline's problems.'

'Sure. You know 'em off by heart!' The man Dominic looked at Amanda as she was standing between Marc's mother and sister. 'You look shocked, little girl!'

'She'd feel better if you'd go!' Jennifer burst out.

'Who is she anyway, or is it some strange secret?'

Elizabeth Chandler drew herself up proudly, though Amanda was aware the old lady was shaking.

'Amanda is coming to us as governess and companion to Karin.'

She made no attempt to introduce them and the man Dominic gave a shout of forced laughter. 'Governess to Caroline—or has Marc fallen in love at last?' He laughed again and Amanda instinctively recoiled. 'What are you, girlie with the big green eyes, blind? Don't you know you're in danger?'

'I know you're terribly confused!' she retorted, speaking for the first time. She was finding it difficult to focus on the man's narrow, half agonised face. As Caroline's cousin, he was enough like her to be handsome in a weak, cruel way and he had Caroline's glittering pale eyes.

'Don't get mixed up with this noble family, girlie. Caro will tear you to pieces!'

'Do exactly what I say!' Ross Fullerton ordered sternly, advancing on the other man. 'Get out and take your vile suggestions with you!'

'Don't worry, I'm going!' The man Dominic choked and Amanda thought she could even see tears in his eyes. 'Give my regards to Marc!' Hate suddenly blazed in the pale eyes. They swept over everyone, included Amanda, then he started down the stairs, lurching a little as if he were drunk.

'Dear God!' Ross Fullerton breathed like a prayer.

Elizabeth Chandler became aware of the white-faced girl beside her. 'I'm so sorry, Amanda. I wouldn't have had that happen for the world. Dominic rarely comes to this house any more, though he was in and out of it all the time as a growing boy. Dominic is Caroline's cousin, Dominic O'Neill. Their mothers were sisters. Dominic is rather a tragic person really, weak and unstable, but he does care for Caroline in his way. The thing is we consider him a bad influence, but we can't protect Caroline all the time. She's a grown woman and Dominic is a member of her own family. As soon as Marc comes down again, you'll want to go. Please try to disregard anything Dominic said to upset you. That's his speciality, and he gives most of his attention to this family.'

'When they were boys he used to idolise Marc, do you remember?' Jennifer was almost talking to herself.

'Both Dominic and Caroline can hate and love with equal ferocity!' her husband said behind her, his pleasant dependable face creased with worry. 'Look here, young lady, I think we should drive you home. Poor old Marc has more than enough on his hands!'

'I'll stay with Mamma!' said Jennifer, furious to see her mother's hands shaking. 'Please don't let that little episode change anything, Amanda. We really do need you, and Karin surely does!'

Amanda looked back sympathetically at the elegant young woman beside her, though she was feeling shaken and exhausted herself. 'I'm only sorry to see you all so upset, especially Mrs Chandler. I've agreed to come and I will. We'll take each day as it comes and I promise to do my very best. Of course it mightn't be good enough and if things aren't going to work out, then I guess we'll all know.'

'I suppose so!' Jennifer sighed deeply. 'I was feeling so ... so settled in my mind. You were everything we hoped for, Amanda, but now I'm troubled again. I'd better stay home and look after my own child at least!'

'Oh, really, darling!' Ross Fullerton looked completely off balance. 'What's the use of letting O'Neill upset us? He's never been any good for anything else, and nothing changes with Caroline. I haven't had you with me on a trip since our honeymoon and you can't know how I'm looking forward to this. Please don't say no, for God's sake. Pip will give no one any trouble and he wants to stay with Gran and Karin and Marc. You *will* stay, won't you, Amanda?'

'Don't pressure the girl!' Marc Chandler ordered abruptly from behind them. 'Who could blame her if she doesn't?' He came down the last few stairs looking inexpressibly disciplined, a man who kept an iron rein on his emotions. 'Get Mamma a brandy, Jen, and I'll take Amanda home. You might wait until I get back. Ross, I have something I want you to do for me.'

'Surely,' Ross offered. 'How's Caroline?'

'Out cold!' his brother-in-law returned with a frightening indifference. 'If you're ready, Amanda, we'll go.'

Outside in the car he told her almost curtly to fasten the seat belt, then he swung the wheel and they were heading down the long drive to the massive wrought iron fence that guarded the street entrance of the property. Amanda sat tensed up beside him, not daring to glance at his splendid, set profile. He seemed utterly ruthless, and she found it in her heart to pity his wife. Probably he treated her abominably, yet he had the unquestioned love and respect of his family and indeed the town. Perhaps there were two sides to him, the ruthlessness, the latent sensuality and the inherent pride in family. His mother adored him and Elizabeth Chandler was a woman who could not love without respect. It was all very difficult.

He never spoke a word to her until they reached Amanda's home, then he switched off the engine and turned to her. 'I've decided, Amanda, you won't suit after all.' He leaned over and opened her door and for an instant she could feel the hard strength of his arm locking her body to the seat, making contact with the tilted curves of her breasts. 'I'm sorry,' he said flatly, 'but that's the way it is and no real harm done. You'll continue at the Medical Centre as usual, but I'd like to pay you for what inconvenience I've caused you.'

'Thank you, but *no!*' she cried emphatically, dismayed by the childish tremble in her voice. 'I understand perfectly, Mr Chandler. Goodnight, and may I say I'm sorry for everyone, except you!'

'Of course I'm the black-haired villian,' he agreed with quiet anger. 'That's all right, little one, I'm used to it. Go inside now. I can only harm you!'

Something in his voice stayed her, some note she had never heard before, almost a tenderness, as if he really did care. 'But I don't understand!' She swung back to look at him, leaning a little closer in an attempt to see his eyes. It was very dark with only a few windy stars and his own tension was very close to the surface.

For a crazy moment Amanda wondered what was happening to her, because she was trembling violently, making a public show of her helpless attraction to him no matter what he was—a sadist, a wife-beater. She was frightened and mistrustful, yet her body was aching, almost wanting to be bruised. She even feared she was in a dream state, painfully conscious of his nearness and the way one brown, long-fingered hand rested along the back of the seat. The unnatural quality of the silence was making her heart and her pulse go wild. No one she had ever met had such power to excite such deep and changing emotions.

'Go inside!' he said again, and the dark decisive voice went curiously harsh, sending vibrations through her head.

'What a cruel man you are!' Tears sprang to her eyes and she drew back in agitation, feeling incredibly humiliated. 'How could I ever remain here with *you*?'

'Yes, you little fool, isn't that what I'm trying to tell you?' He moved then like a panther while she froze in torment, unable to move. He pulled her to him with irresistible strength, pinning her silken head with his hand, displaying her face. 'I'm quite sure I can't let you go now!'

'Oh *no*!' she whispered vehemently, terrified now of what would occur.

'You can't escape me,' he said in an undertone. 'Do you know what it's like, Amanda, to find no water in the desert? No life. No love. No woman to sleep with. No silken, yielding flesh pledging the kind of passion I want!'

'This is madness!' she whispered.

'I know. You should have expected it!' He lowered his head and parted her mouth and her stricken sigh faded into the wind. She could feel herself shaking in his arms while he searched her young mouth as if for the very elixir of life.

It was ravishing, and thereafter she was to be torn daily by the answering passion she showed him. Her imprisoned heart was beating wildly to escape. It *was* madness, a brilliant violent turbulence, but no nightmare because he filled her with flame, possessed her, so that her limbs had no power. She was aware of nothing, of no one else, only this dangerous proud man who continued to kiss her mouth with a depth of passion that should have frightened her.

It was a spinning eternity before he drew away. 'You see?' Very gently he touched her arching throat. 'What do you know of life, little one? Of violence and ugly, self-inflicted anguish. You're a mere babe with a future, and I wish you'd let me do something about it.'

'How can I?' She had to lie against him because her trembling limbs still refused to function.

'Easily,' he said. 'Do what I'm telling you. Pick out any university you like and go there in the New Year. Find yourself somewhere to live first. I'll open an account for you and you can pay me back in a few years' time. You being you, I know you'll try to. This is my world, here, Amanda, and there can't be any place for you.'

'But you're driving me away from all I've ever known!'

'No,' he contradicted, 'I'm persuading you for your own good. You're a clever girl. Go ahead and make us all proud of you. Later on you can write a novel or something.'

'One has to know about life. As you've pointed out, I don't actually know about anything.'

'You know what you're capable of,' he said, moving her back to the other seat and holding her away from him. 'Nothing is easy, absolutely nothing. I simply made the mistake of thinking you could help—or rather I allowed myself a temporary aberration.'

'Please don't say any more,' she begged him. 'I'm feeling damaged enough already. I imagine you'll tell your family what you've decided.'

'I will!' he returned with his old confident arrogance. 'Now what about you, Amanda, are you going to do as I ask?'

'Naturally you expect me to, but I'm afraid not, Mr Chandler. Believe me, I'll never cause you a moment of embarrassment, but I refuse to accept what you're offering. There are more important things in life than going to a university. At least I seem to be needed at the Centre.' She dipped her head and slid gracefully out of the car. 'Goodnight! I won't ever remember a thing about tonight!'

'Neither will I,' he announced with an odd humour.

Amanda didn't remain standing. She fled through the dark, inspired night wrapped in sorrow and rage and unthinkable dreams. Hours later when she finally fell into an exhausted sleep her pillow was wet with tears.

It wasn't difficult for Amanda to find out when Jennifer and Ross Fullerton left on their overseas trip. Their photograph appeared in the social section of the week-end papers although neither of them looked overjoyed at the prospect. Through the grapevine too she discovered a nurse-companion had been hired for the house, but to which Mrs Chandler no one seemed to know.

To take her mind off things Amanda allowed Rob to take her out more frequently than she should have. She knew perfectly well she could never come to care for him as more than an attractive and amusing companion, but strangely for Rob, he seemed quite satisfied with this. As for herself, she had lost all her old tranquillity. Her mind and her memory refused to remain in the present, reliving an incident that should never have happened. Though she never even caught sight of him in the following weeks Amanda was shocked to find Marc Chandler's almost tangible presence beside her. He haunted her, so that she grew increasingly to realise what it was like to be obsessed. The cruel fact was that she had allowed him to infatuate her body and mind when he was a man who could dispense with unwanted involvements at will. Perhaps when she was thirty-four or five she might have learnt something of the same talent. Now at nineteen, almost twenty, she was suffering, with no way to end it.

During the week it was fairly easy to lose herself with work. She even went so far as to reorganise the office and devise a foolproof filing system so that even Rob could find any card that he wanted within a fraction of his usual time. Life was full of good things, Amanda told herself, and eventually her world would come right again. No one had betrayed her. She had betrayed herself. In the meantime, she lost weight and turned from a relatively carefree young girl into a woman with secrets in her eyes and a legacy of heartache. It just didn't seem possible that all this had happened in such a short time, but of course it had. Marc Chandler's shadow had fallen across her path and altered the course of her life.

It was two weeks before Christmas when old Mrs Chandler suffered a mild heart attack that precipitated its own course of events. It had been a busy day at the Centre with an unusual spate of minor accidents caused by a combination of heat and high humidity and the school holidays, and Amanda was looking forward to the simple physical pleasure of having a late afternoon swim. When the call came in on the switchboard she knew the split second before she answered it that it came from the Chandler house.

'Doctor McGilvray, please. *Immediately*. Mrs Elizabeth Chandler has had a bad turn.'

It was a woman's voice, clipped and professional, and Amanda put the call through without any preliminary announcement. In another minute Doctor McGilvray came rushing from his office, signalling to Amanda with an urgent, uplifted hand.

'Come with me, Amanda. You might be needed.'

On the rushed trip out to the river road he told her Karin had chosen that very day for one of her renowned tantrums, playing up 'abominably' on her grandmother, and Mrs Caroline Chandler, who could not disguise her fear of illness, had been made to lie down in her room.

'And Marc?' Amanda asked gravely, not even realising she had used his christian name.

'He'll probably beat us back to the house. The nurse has rung him in any case. How that man got saddled with such a wife and child I'll never know. What's the use of being rich and important when there's not a minute of peace in the home?'

'He couldn't leave them,' Amanda explained. 'They need him.'

'Dead ends everywhere!' the doctor sighed, and put a hand to the back of his neck. 'When we get there, I want you to take charge of the children. The nurse sounds efficient, but she told me quite flatly that she can't cope with Karin. Just keep them quiet and pray to God the young Mrs Chandler keeps out of the way.'

When they arrived at the house, the staff were standing about in the entrance hall obviously waiting for the doctor. Relief flashed into their faces when they saw him and Mrs Harper, the housekeeper, went to say something, but Doctor McGilvray held up a hand and ran like a young man up the broad flight of stairs.

'Miss Raymond!' Brenda came from behind the ample form of the housekeeper to seize Amanda's arm. 'It's terrible, isn't it? We're all so upset. Young Mrs Chandler made me feel so guilty, so negligent....'

'Look here, Brenda,' Mrs Harper interrupted, 'she just got uptight. We're all pretty edgy!' She looked from Brenda to the silent Amanda. 'I'm glad you're here, miss. The doctor promised he'd bring you to look after the children. Young Karin was bawling madly the last time I saw her.'

'And where is she?' Amanda looked up to the next floor instinctively.

'If you must know I had to lock them in the schoolroom. Things were pretty chaotic, and I had to do something.' She delved into her uniform pocket and came up with a key, handing it to Amanda and pressing it into her palm. 'Do your best, love, and do it quickly. You're dealing with a highly unpredictable child, the poor little scrap.'

'Shall I take you up, miss?' Brenda asked anxiously.

'No, it's all right, I know the way.'

Mrs Harper's pleasant face sharpened. 'In my day they used to say boys will be boys, now girls are just girls, aren't they? I mean, they even threaten you.' She stared before her for a moment lost in grim thought, then she signalled to the others to clear the entrance hall. 'Mr Chandler will be here in a moment. We can't be standing around here talking.'

Amanda crossed the beautiful terrazzo floor and begin to walk up the stairs. She had only seen Karin once, but she couldn't imagine why one small girl was dumbfounding so many adults. As she walked down the corridor of the east wing she could hear the impassioned pounding on the schoolroom door, It would be a miracle if Karin didn't rush her and knock her down.

'Stop that!' she called firmly, and inserted the key in the door, turning it slowly in an effort to control one small girl's possible wild haste. There was no violent exodus and she shut the door after her, turning to look at the two small whitened faces that contemplated her speechlessly.

'Hello, children, were you having a bad time of it?'

The little boy moved suddenly, making up his mind. 'Boy, you can say that again! I was just praying for a miracle. How's Granny?'

Amanda looked down at him, at the dark rumpled curls and the frightened brown eyes, and drew him to her, keeping an arm around his shoulder. 'The doctor is here, dear. You're Pip, aren't you? I'm Amanda.'

'Don't be a fool, Pip!' Karin shrieked. 'Come away from her!'

Amanda's arm tightened still more about the little boy while he rested gently against her. 'We've got our miracle,' he said almost severely, 'you're the fool.'

Karin was full of resentment and terror, her blue eyes staring. 'She's dead, isn't she? You've come to tell us she's dead and I killed her!'

A lump rose in Amanda's throat as she gazed at the small impassioned face, then she put out her other hand, speaking very gently.

'Come here, Karin. Come here to me. I promise you

Granny is going to be all right.' Inwardly she was murmuring prayers of her own because she had no way of knowing Mrs Chandler's true condition.

Karin's eyelids flickered and the half anguished, half defiant little face went tremulous. 'You wouldn't lie to me, would you?'

'How could anyone be so cruel! Of course I'm not, Karin. I told you, Doctor McGilvray is with Granny now and your father is coming here just as soon as he can.' Still holding out her hand, she kept her eyes on Karin's face, willing the small girl into some kind of calm.

'I truly never meant it to happen!' The pale blue eyes were huge and still.

'Of course you didn't!' Amanda said soothingly.

'Look, Karin!' Pip burst out confidentially, 'the doctor is here to save her and 'Manda let us out.'

Karin tried to speak, but all she could manage was a series of hiccoughing gasps. 'Quick, Pip, pour Karin a glass of water!' Amanda ordered briskly, giving the little boy something to do.

He let go her hand and made a rush for the water jug, while Amanda started walking towards Karin slowly and steadily. She was almost there when Pip put the glass of water into her hand.

'Here, dear. Have a drink of water.'

She waited a few seconds before Karin took the glass from her hand, drinking deeply and keeping her shining upward glance on Amanda's face. 'Thank you.'

'Do you feel better now?'

'Yes,' said Karin, and gave the empty glass back to her cousin.

'Gee, you're a nut sometimes!' Pip said affectionately.

'Mummy said Gran was going to die!' Karin announced urgently. There was desperation in her voice and Amanda heard it.

'*Karin!*' she exclaimed, then crouched down beside the little girl. 'When your grandmother is feeling better, I'm going to take you to see her. She's resting now and Doctor McGilvray will probably give her something so she can have a little sleep. Afterwards you and Pip and I will slip into her room for a few moments while you tell her how much you love her.'

'Oh, I *do*!' Karin blinked her swimming eyes, as if she was very tired, and Amanda reached out and patted her wet cheek gently.

'Don't think your grandmother doesn't know that. Keep it in mind, because you see, dear, we have to stay very quiet while Granny has her rest.'

'How long?' Karin asked weakly. 'It's dreadful here. I want Daddy!'

'And you're going to have him. He may even be home now, but we're all going to behave so we won't worry him any more.'

'You'll stay, won't you?' Karin whispered, and put a hand over Amanda's fingers. 'I won't get into any trouble if you stay. Mummy will tell Daddy I've been very bad again!'

'That's right!' Pip confirmed, nodding judiciously. 'Karin has a different kind of mother from mine.'

'I'm wicked!' Karin added brokenly.

'What rubbish!' Amanda drew the little girl right into her arms and Karin didn't break away. 'Who could ever believe that about such a beautiful little girl?'

'Your hair smells nice,' Karin muttered. 'I was hoping and hoping you'd come back.'

'Really?' Amanda's satin skin faintly flushed.

Karin didn't answer, but sighed deeply, burying her face under Amanda's chin. 'Suppose we go and have a look at Granny now?' she finally murmured, and straightened up. The blue eyes were pleading and still full of fright.

'Why don't you stay here for a minute with Pip while I go and see,' Amanda said evenly, her eyes keen on the child's face. Karin was quite capable of tearing after her, disturbing the household.

'I don't want you to leave us.'

'I'll be here!' said Pip, and smiled so sweetly at Amanda that she was entranced.

'Not *you*!' Karin said with quiet scorn. 'You're just a little boy!'

'Oh, pardon!' said Pip, and Karin was immediately contrite.

'But you're a good little kid. It's true—everyone says so. I get into trouble all the time.'

'No wonder!' Pip exclaimed.

It was the wrong thing to say because Karin's white skin went vivid over the cheekbones. 'If you don't want to stay here why don't you go away? This is *my* home.'

'And Pip is your guest,' Amanda pointed out gently. 'Come, if you promise me to be very quiet we'll go and ask after your grandmother.'

Both children looked up at her, instantly alert. Pip came to stand beside her, slipping one trusting hand into her own, and after a minute, as if it was the only sensible thing to do, Karin followed suit. 'Don't worry,' she said, and raised her eyes to Amanda, 'I'll behave. Granny's going to live because of you.'

'Not *me*, darling!'

'Yes, *you!*' Karin retorted, convinced. 'You're the very first miracle that's ever happened.'

Amanda was genuinely startled, but she said nothing. Both children obviously believed she had come in answer to their prayers, and who knows, perhaps she had? Karin was just the type of child to push herself into hysteria, while even an entrancing little boy like Pip was showing signs of strain.

When they were out in the corridor Amanda looked down at them, breathing a barely audible: 'Ssh now!'

Pip picked up his sandalled feet and Karin tightened her clutch on Amanda's hand. There seemed to be no sound anywhere in the house and Amanda felt her heart beating uneasily. How dreadful it would be if Mrs Chandler hadn't responded to treatment. She couldn't even bear to think of it, with at least one little hand breaking out into a cold sweat. She half expected to see Brenda or Mrs Harper coming towards them, shaking their heads mournfully. She didn't know it, but she had turned very pale herself.

At the top of the stairs, Karin's frail control broke. 'I can't see anyone, can you? Perhaps we're all alone in the house?'

The same terrible alarm began to fill Amanda, but she forced herself to speak quietly. 'Now, Karin, didn't I promise you everything will be all right? We'll just go downstairs.'

They reached the landing before Marc Chandler walked into the entrance hall from the library and threw up his head. He looked at Amanda with his brilliant eyes, then he looked at the children, holding tight to her hands.

'Your mother?' Amanda whispered, feeling she

couldn't endure it for the children's sake if the news was bad.

'Resting quietly,' he said gravely, though his dark eyes were intent, almost piercing in their regard.

'Thank God!' Her knees were a little unsteady. 'The children have been so worried. May I bring them down?'

'Yes,' he said.

Nothing could keep Karin away from him. She broke Amanda's hold and flew on down the stairs, desperate for her father's love and comfort. He caught her small flying body and lifted her in his arms while she twined her arms round his neck as though she couldn't bear to let him go.

'*Daddy!*'

Pip was next. He padded down the stairs after his cousin and leaned against Marc's long legs, looking up at him. 'I kept telling Karin there'd be a miracle, then 'Manda arrived.'

'So she did!' said Marc, his expression unreadable. 'All of you look as if you should be taken straight to the kitchen and fed. I've never seen such white faces.'

Amanda still hesitated with her hand on the banister. 'Has Doctor McGilvray gone?'

'Not yet.' He glanced away from his daughter and up at Amanda standing so quietly. 'My mother should really go to hospital for a period of complete rest, but we can't persuade her to leave the house.'

'No!' Amanda shook her head compassionately. She could see Elizabeth Chandler resisting even when ill. 'I've promised the children I'd take them in to see her later on, just for a few seconds to reassure them. I hope I did right?'

'Why not? It will make everyone feel better. Come down, Amanda, you look very fragile standing there.'

'I feel it!'

It wasn't good to be desperate for the sight of a man called Marc Chandler. She made an elaborate effort to appear normal, not knowing her face was young and exquisitely transparent.

Marc was silent watching her and Pip looked up at his uncle and gave his beatific smile. ''Manda's going to stay with us!' he announced, sounding enormously cheered.

'I had this mad idea I might be able to help for a little while,' Amanda explained quickly.

Karin lifted her silky dark head and drew a long, shaky breath. 'She will, won't she, Daddy?'

Marc was very slow in answering, his eyes brooding on Amanda's creamy-skinned face. 'Until your mother is feeling a little better,' Amanda repeated, her green eyes full of concern.

Before Marc could answer, Doctor McGilvray came down the stairs followed by a plain, efficient-looking woman dressed in a pale blue uniform.

'There you are, Marc!' the doctor exclaimed, then his glance embraced Amanda and the children. 'Cheer up, everyone, our patient gave us a little fright, that's all!'

'And has she consented to go to hospital?' Marc asked, and lowered Karin gently to the floor.

'No, she hasn't,' Doctor McGilvray answered bluntly. 'You know your mother, Marc! Still, we should be able to manage between us, and I see the children are being very good.'

'When can I see her?' Karin asked in a small voice full of pleading.

'Well now. . . .' The doctor lifted a hand and buried it in his white shock of hair, obviously hesitating, and Karin flung herself sideways, grasping Amanda around her narrow waist.

'You *promised* us!'

'So I did!' Unconsciously Amanda's voice softened. 'But we have to wait patiently until Doctor McGilvray says yes.'

The doctor raised his brows, but his eyes were kind and understanding. 'You seem to have made the decision for me, Amanda. Very well, a little later on. Nurse will tell you when.' He looked up the curving stairway towards the waiting nurse and she came down to join them.

Marc took over and introduced the two women, and Amanda found herself being examined thoroughly if not critically.

'How do you do, Miss Raymond?' The voice was low and almost flat.

Amanda knew instantly she wasn't liked, so she wasn't surprised when the nurse added virtuously, 'It might be a good thing if you and the children waited until the morning.'

'On the contrary,' Marc Chandler bent his brilliant black regard on her, 'my mother would wish to see them tonight, if it's at all possible.'

'If you say so, sir!'

Though the tone was respectful, even diffident, again it alerted Amanda to strange undercurrents. She glanced at the doctor for confirmation and he said soothingly: 'I know I can rely on you, Amanda, to judge the situation. Now, if you've got a few more minutes, Marc, there are a few things I'd like to tell you, then I must be on my way. The Laceys' first is due to make its appearance.'

'In that case come through to the library.' Marc turned and led the way, while the doctor followed, flinging a few hasty words over his shoulder. 'Don't go away, Amanda, you can walk down to the car with me.'

'Do I take it you're staying, Miss Raymond?' Nurse Mellon asked with such peculiar insolence Amanda was rasped to anger.

'For a few days,' she said, fighting back the desire to tell the nurse to mind her own business.

This was received with a thin smile. 'You'll have a job on your hands with the children.'

'I don't think so!'

'Why should she?' Pip asked quickly. 'We can have fun.'

'Fun?' Nurse Mellon repeated the word dubiously. 'I know this young lady here has nearly driven her poor mother crazy, not to speak of her grandmother. Now I have two charges. I'm here to look after Miss Caroline, you know. She's always been terribly delicate and so high-strung she can't have any kind of strain. She's so beautiful, isn't she? The loveliest person I've ever seen.'

'You've known her for some time?' Amanda asked politely.

'From childhood, Miss Raymond. I was with Mrs Langland, Caroline's mother, at the end. We became very close, though I was only the nurse. Then Caroline asked me to come to her and of course I said yes. There's nothing I wouldn't do to make her lot easier.'

'How sweet!' said Amanda, and glanced down at the definitely belligerent Karin. 'It must mean a lot to her to know you're here.'

'Yes,' Nurse Mellon agreed, 'it does.' Her lips were very tight and she studied Amanda's face rather grimly. 'It's hard to believe you look after children.'

'I'm the receptionist at the Medical Centre—didn't Doctor McGilvray tell you?'

'No.' Nurse Mellon's curiously opaque grey eyes met Amanda's. 'He merely told me he was bringing someone to look after the children. You must be very clever!'

'You'd be surprised how much!' Amanda said modestly. 'Ah, here comes Doctor McGilvray. You'll excuse us, won't you, Nurse? The children can play in the garden while I'm speaking to the doctor.'

'As you like,' Nurse Mellon said indifferently. 'I'm here to look out for Miss Caroline.'

'And Mrs Chandler too, I hope?' Amanda said sharply.

'Of course!' the nurse returned, equally sharp.

'*Amanda!*' Doctor McGilvray's voice was touched with briskness.

She caught the children by the hand and they went willingly, Karin venturing a wry: 'Yuck!' before she was scarcely out the door. 'I hate her. She's got eyes like pebbles!'

Pip began to laugh and Amanda pushed them gently before her. 'Go and play on the swing for a while. I have to see the doctor.'

'I'll race you!' Pip called to his cousin, already speeding across the grass while Karin lingered behind.

'I'm sorry I said that about your hair the last time.' said the little girl.

'That's all right!' Amanda said with a soft little laugh.

'I really *love* it. I had a doll with long blonde hair like yours, but she died.'

'Oh, I'm sorry!' Amanda murmured, and looked back at the child with gentle eyes. 'You might be able to tell me about it some time.'

'Yes,' smiled Karin, and ran off.

Doctor McGilvray was waiting, standing by the car door. 'A pretty kettle of fish!' he commented when Amanda reached him.

'I think maybe you're talking about Nurse Mellon.'

'Partly, but she's competent enough. She'll look after our patient, don't worry about that. After all, she is a good nurse, I've checked on that. The thing is she's one-eyed about her Miss Caroline. Doesn't seem to notice she's all grown up, or should be. Never mind. You seem to have the children in hand. Keep it up like a good girl, at least until Mrs Chandler is stronger.'

'And how *is* she?' Amanda asked earnestly.

'Vulnerable!' the doctor answered. 'She's been a wonderful woman in her day, still is, but she's being worn out. The attack was a mild one, but it was a warning. It could happen again. She tells me she'll be seventy in March—and that's the first time I ever got that out of her!' The sure, capable hands opened the car door and the doctor heaved himself into the driving seat. 'Do what you can, Amanda, use all your gifts for diplomacy, and if it all gets too much for you, sing out. I'll be in and out of the house anyway until Elizabeth is up and about. She likes you and she seems eager that you stay. I told her I brought you along. When you meet the young Mrs Chandler, don't forget you're dealing with an unpredictable temperament. Make allowances, but don't let her browbeat you. The reason you're here is to look after the children and, indirectly, my patient.'

'I understand!'

'Good girl. Frankly I've always found you equal to any occasion!' The doctor started the motor and Amanda stood back waving. Doctor McGilvray might consider her capable, but there was no great confidence in her now. It was dreary but true, Nurse Mellon would never be an ally and she had no means of knowing how Mrs Caroline Chandler would greet her. The only thing to do was go right back in there and find out.

The children tumbled off the swing and ran towards her and together they walked back towards the splendid white house, scattered lights now glinting against the upstairs windows.

'Can you swim, Amanda?' Pip asked hopefully.

'I *can't*!' said Karin, almost fearfully.

'You can't?' Amanda looked down at her in astonishment. 'You have the river and the lake and a swimming pool and you can't swim?'

Pip's brown eyes were trying to convey a warning, but unexpectedly Karin didn't erupt. 'Mummy says she doesn't even dare think about me drowning.'

'But that's the whole point!' Amanda objected. 'It's very difficult indeed for a good swimmer to drown. I'll have to teach you.'

'You'd better be ready for some screams!' Pip raised his hands and put his fingers in his ears. 'The last time Uncle Marc tried to teach her she nearly had convulsions.'

'Perhaps she'll do better with me. What do you say, little Karin?'

Karin knotted her delicate black brows. 'I think there just might be a chance so long as we don't go near the river. That's where Francesca got drowned.'

'Cut it out!' Pip breathed, and stared big-eyed at Amanda. 'You can't drown a *doll*!'

'Yes, you can!' For a split second Karin's voice was as hard and matter-of-fact as her father's. 'And I know exactly who drowned her!'

CHAPTER FIVE

LEE, the Chinese manservant, drove Amanda back to the house so she could collect everything she needed for her stay at the Chandler mansion. It was a fast trip because Amanda was anxious about leaving the children with old Mrs Chandler so recently ill. Lee at least was very friendly and gentle, devoted to Marc Chandler and the Chandler family as much as Nurse Mellon appeared to be devoted to her Miss Caroline. Somehow Amanda managed to get her things together in under an hour and lock up the house, but even that space of time proved too long.

Marc's Mercedes was gone from the driveway but Amanda was barely in the house before she heard Karin's screams. Lee dropped her large suitcase and looked at her. 'You'll have to stop her, missy, with Mrs Chandler so ill. The car is gone, so the master is out. He had arrangements to make with the Mines Manager.'

Amanda, too, dropped her overnight bag and ran up the stairs, heading towards the source of the commotion. Poor Mrs Chandler, to be subjected to all this! She really should have gone to hospital whether she wanted to or not. For everyone's sake Amanda had to succeed with Karin, who undoubtedly was way out of control. Even stranger was that any child of Marc Chandler's could be so overpoweringly undisciplined.

She reached the gallery and looked along the corri-

dor, wanting to cry out to the battling duo to stop.
When she had left Karin the child had been gentled
and almost tractable, but now she was kicking out at
Nurse Mellon in a fury while Nurse Mellon had the
shouting child imprisoned by the wrists.

'You little wretch, you need a sound beating!'

'Let go of me!' Karin raised her voice to a new
decibel, her small face flushed and her eyes red-rimmed.

Amanda almost slashed along the carpet runner to
grasp the nurse's shoulder. 'Let go of her, please.
You'll disturb Mrs Chandler!'

'You mean *you're* going to quiet this little demon?'
Nurse Mellon turned on her, very nearly snarling in
her rage.

Karin just as suddenly stopped shrieking, her great
shining eyes fixed on Amanda's face. 'She wouldn't let
me in to Granny!'

'And she was right!' Amanda returned swiftly. 'A
promise is a promise, Karin. It works both ways, and
you've let both of us down!'

'It's no use, I'm wicked!' Karin burst out.

'Oh, fiddlesticks!' snapped Amanda, 'you just like
to be naughty, but not *now*, Karin, with your father
depending on you to behave yourself and your grandmother so in need of rest. Apologise to Nurse Mellon,
otherwise you won't see your grandmother at all this
evening.'

The radiant blue eyes swept Nurse Mellon's stocky
form briefly. 'I'm sorry!'

'We both know you're *not*!' The muscles under
Nurse Mellon's jaw tightened, then she transferred her
stony gaze to Amanda's anxious face. 'The child does
have a mother, you know, Miss Raymond. You seem to

be forgetting that. A *mother*, Miss Raymond, to whom I'm responsible. It's my duty to report this child. She's entirely out of hand. In fact I've never encountered such shocking disobedience.'

'As you say, Nurse Mellon,' Amanda agreed with gravity, 'Karin *does* have a mother. Unfortunately we haven't met, but she could only be hurt by your pointing out her child's limitations, surely?'

Nurse Mellon shook her head. 'She's quite aware of them, I assure you. You seem to have forgotten Doctor McGilvray left me in charge. I forbid you to go in to Mrs Chandler tonight!'

'She means it!' Karin gasped with what sounded like helpless defeat.

Amanda shrugged, her eyes brilliantly green. '*Mr* Chandler has given his permission, and I take orders from him.'

'I believe so!' Nurse Mellon said meaningfully, and Amanda grasped Karin's nerveless hand, turning about and going down the corridor towards the east wing.

'I'm glad you were there to protect me!' said Karin.

'Really?' Amanda looked down at her with unamused eyes. 'I'd have done so gladly, only it seemed to me Nurse Mellon was getting the worst of it!'

'She has very sadistic hands!' Karin offered, to Amanda's considerable surprise.

'Nonsense, she's merely strong. What does sadistic mean anyway?'

'So you hate people!'

'Goodness, no! I think she was just desperate to quiet you.'

'It wasn't my idea to throw a tantrum,' explained

Karin. 'She just grabbed me and told me she was going to teach me an important lesson.'

'That's *my* job!' Amanda said firmly, and paused at Pip's bedroom door. 'Is this where you left Pip?'

'He went with Daddy. He's very interested in joining the business.'

'And you're not?'

'Of course not. I'm going to be rich when I grow up.'

'What a disability!' Amanda said coolly. 'It's very dull sitting around all day with no job to do.'

'Like Mummy,' Karin said to the now silent house.

Amanda looked along to her own door. 'Oh good, Lee has brought my things up. Why don't you come and help me put them away? I've got something for you, as a matter of fact.'

'I hate surprises!' Karin remarked, but went gladly through Amanda's door.

'Your room's pretty, isn't it?' she commented.

'Yes, it is,' Amanda agreed. 'I've never slept in a fourposter in my life.'

'That's strange for a princess!' Karin went to the armchair and sat down. 'That's what you look like, a princess in a fairytale. I can show you some of my books. They have beautiful illustrations. Mummy looks like the Queen in Snow White, before she got wicked, that is. Everyone tells me I'm going to look exactly like Mummy when I grow up.'

'Then you're a very lucky girl. Your mother is a very beautiful woman.'

Karin laughed. 'I wish she was nice as well.'

'*Darling!*' Amanda just managed not to drop the pile of clothes in her hands.

'True!' Karin insisted, seeing Amanda was shocked.

'You mustn't make her angry whatever you do. May I help you?' She got up to join Amanda at the gleaming chest of drawers.

'You can put some of those dresses on hangers if you like.'

'Pass me the hangers,' said Karin. 'You always look so pretty, but you don't have lovely dresses like Mummy. She has masses and masses of everything, then she throws everything out in a pile. I heard Daddy say once when he was angry that Mummy is only serious about spending money. That's why she stays with him, she likes it so much.'

Amanda was determined not to follow up that line of conversation. She went to her overnight bag and pulled out a charming, frivolous fan that she had found in one of the old trunks in the spare room at home. It was lavishly decorated with birds and flowers and a series of simpering Oriental ladies.

'This is for you when you're hot!'

'For me?' Karin clapped her hands delightedly, her small face pure and sweet. 'It's a beauty, isn't it? I've never had a fan before.'

'You'll need it when the sun comes out,' Amanda told her lightly. 'Especially with that beautiful complexion.'

Karin began to wave it gracefully to and fro as if she'd been doing it all her life. 'The house is air-conditioned, you know!'

'That cuts me down to size!'

Karin laughed and immediately Amanda laughed too. 'I must congratulate you on the way you're handling it!'

Karin danced up to glance in the mirror, obviously

dazzled with herself, when her father's voice sounded sternly through the open doorway.

'So there you are!'

Karin swung around, half subdued. 'Yes, Daddy. I was helping Amanda put her things away.'

'That's not what *I* heard!' he said, and made a sharp impatient sound. He looked past Karin's little face to Amanda. 'Why is it that I can never walk out of this house and anticipate a normal return?'

Amanda stood there, blonde and slender, her eyes probing the dark contours of his face. 'Does that imply some criticism of me?'

'Either it's going to work or it's not!' he said forcibly. 'Nurse Mellon has just waylaid me in the hall, unburdening herself. It was scarcely bearable, what with trying to save us all and everything and Kat running wild. So far as she's concerned we can dispense with your services at once!'

'Perhaps she's right,' Amanda said shakily. 'There's no need for violence. I'll go without a struggle.'

'Great!' he flashed back with black humour. 'You're going to get emotional as well.'

Karin stared anxiously from one to the other, then she launched herself at Amanda, jerking on her hand imploringly. 'You can't *possibly*!' she exclaimed.

'I don't want to!'

'Just tell me what really happened,' Marc asked wearily. 'I see Kat now loves you, or presumes she loves you.'

'It is heartening!' Amanda agreed, and collapsed into a chair. 'You know Karin has been anxious to see her grandmother, she just jumped the gun, that's all. I arrived back in time to check her. Nurse Mellon's tactics weren't working.'

'It's not her job, after all,' he said, and shrugged his wide shoulders. 'How depressing that grown women can't manage one small child.'

'Couldn't you have taken Karin with you?' Amanda asked, not moving her eyes from him.

'I don't believe she wanted to come. Are you taking *me* to task now?'

'I'm just pointing out a possible course you could have taken.'

'Hasn't it occurred to you that my meeting demanded my undivided attention?'

'You took Pip,' she pointed out.

'I know!' he said, and suddenly relaxed. 'Pip is a nice sober little fellow. I'd be proud to own him.'

Karin gave a hopeless shake of her head and her father glanced down at her. 'What is it, baby?'

No answer.

He dropped into the chair opposite Amanda and pulled the child into his arms. 'Come on, spit it out!'

Another headshake, then Karin began to cry—soft, sad, hopeless little sobs.

'Is it something I've done? Something I've said? Is it Gran?'

'Perhaps it's important you tell her you're proud to own her as well!' Amanda offered softly.

'Is it *that*?' Marc asked his daughter with honest interest.

Karin clutched him even closer and nodded her head.

'But, baby, you have pride of place. Nobody else!'

If it was a slip he didn't notice it and Amanda thought how deeply wounding it would be to be his wife. How wounding and strange, because the tenderness in his face, and the intensely attractive inflection in his voice, was turning her own heart over, let alone Karin's. She leaned her blonde head back against the armchair and watched them. Karin's passionate sobs had broken off. She had a blind arm around her father's neck and her face was pressed against his chest.

Marc lifted his eyes to her and for a moment Amanda could feel her heartbeats almost directly in her eardrums. The half smile on his mouth was replaced by a mocking light in his heavily lashed dark eyes. They slipped coolly over Amanda, almost experimentally, and she had the unutterable sensation that he was touching her.

'So you're here!' he said, and his voice was barely above an undertone.

Her green eyes were shimmering and wary in her young unguarded face. She was afraid to answer and she knew he sensed that, for he gave a brief ironic laugh.

'Amanda to the rescue!'

'You're not angry?' she managed.

'There's no use talking about it. I'm overwhelmed!' Karin was still in her wonderful trancelike state and Marc spoke gently into the top of her head. 'Wipe the tears away, baby. I gather you're going in to see your grandmother.'

'Oh, please, Daddy!' Karin raised her silky dark head.

'Run along, then, and tidy yourself up. Then keep Pip company until I come for you. Understood?'

'Yes!' Karin answered with conviction. 'Is Amanda coming too?'

'Yes. I can't fight her.'

'You're funny!' Karin called as she skipped through the door.

There was a significant silence after she had gone, then a heightening tension that Amanda couldn't wish out of existence. Marc was standing in the middle of the room, his dark eyes brilliant beneath the slanting black brows, the light glossing the bronze sheen of his skin, a muscle tautening beside the hard, cleanly cut mouth.

'There's no wisdom in asking you to help me thrash out my little problems.'

'You did before!' Her own expression changed at the terse inflection in his voice.

'That was before I had the insane notion to make love to you.'

'I'm quite sure you won't want to again.'

'What do *you* think?' he said disagreeably. 'You're the kind of woman a man likes to make suffer for the sheer pleasure of kissing her better, too soft and desirable. I knew immediately I walked in that I should have marched you right out.'

'You can still do that!' The colour leapt into her skin, and she jumped to her feet looking very tender and hurt. 'I hope Karin will understand. You tell her —I can't.'

'Then I'd best get to it!' he said with arrogant simplicity. 'I can't have you involved.'

'But I am!'

'Not deeply!' he demanded, his eyes narrowing over her tortured face.

Like Karin she couldn't answer him and he said almost gently: 'Come here to me, little one.'

She flushed alarmingly and ran her tongue along her top lip to gain precious seconds. The man who regarded her was no longer darkly remote. There was sensuality in his face as he allowed himself to look at her, a cruel-to-be-kind expression that nevertheless infused a heady excitement into her veins.

To her horror he closed the distance that separated them, lifting his hand, the tips of his fingers caressing her scalp, holding her face up to him. 'You're not afraid of me, then?'

Her green eyes were startlingly beautiful, huge and troubled. 'You know I am.'

'It would be so easy to ruin your life, but I won't do it.'

'I only want to help you!' Her heart was beating madly against her breast and she knew if he suddenly swung her up into his arms she would go with him anywhere.

'No!' he said harshly, and tugged her head back painfully.

Tears rushed into her eyes and she gave a little muffled protest. 'Please, Marc, let me go!'

'I didn't say you could call me Marc in that sweet little girl voice!'

'Oh, *please*!' she begged again, because he was still holding her, hurting her.

'For you—anything!' he said with a hard bitterness. 'You're half in love with me, aren't you?'

'Damn you, I'm not!' She drew back from him, her blonde hair dishevelled. 'You're a cruel man. A cruel, *married* man!'

'If I was as cruel as you say, then why don't I let you stay?' His voice controlled now, bitingly sarcastic.

'I won't bother you in any way!' Amanda threw up her hands and covered her face as though shutting out his savagely disturbing presence.

'I know you mean that, Amanda, but it mightn't quite come off. You're a beautiful girl and I'm a ruthless man, aren't I?'

'You can be very tender with your daughter,' she said, and it sounded utterly melancholy. 'I would like to see your mother. She was very kind to me. She sent me a little note—did you know?'

'It sounds like her,' he said, a shade wryly. 'It was no small thing to prevent her from going round to see you. Jenny happened to leave a letter for you as well.'

'I didn't get it!' she turned to him with quick distress.

'I'm not surprised. I tore it up.'

'You had no right!' she said fervently, and brushed a single tear off her smooth petalled cheek.

Marc's brief laugh was ironic. 'My dear child, I have your best interests at heart. It's obvious you don't know how to take care of yourself.' He moved to the door with a swiftness that made her dizzy. 'For God's sake,' his voice taunted her, 'you're tearing yourself to pieces *now*. Stay a day or two, Amanda, I can take it. Then you're definitely going home and I'm sorry, but I'm not going to have you at the Centre. I wanted to help you the first time I ever saw you and you were just a child. I want to help you now, though you won't believe it. My initial arrangement for your future suits me fine. Think about it. I always get my way.'

'Not with me!' she exclaimed, and her inner intensity was etched on her face.

'You're very brave with the room between us!'

His attraction for her was a frightening thing and she turned away in a near frenzy to pick up her silver backed hairbrush and draw it ruthlessly through her tumbled hair. She could still feel the touch of his fingers against her scalp.

Amanda was unprepared for the deep sincerity of old Mrs Chandler's welcome. She lay back against the pillows looking much older and frailer than the last time Amanda had seen her. The children had been allowed to see her for a moment and kiss her good-night, then Marc had signalled to Brenda to come and prepare them for bedtime. They went quietly, much subdued by their grandmother's evident fragility, and Amanda guessed neither of them would give the slightest trouble that night. Even Brenda's doubts about her ability to handle Karin melted from her eyes.

When the children had gone and the door was closed again, Mrs Chandler called Amanda closer to the bed, searching the lovely, intelligent young face that was observing her with so much concern and compassion.

'It's a great comfort to me, Amanda, to know you're here,' she whispered.

'There's no need to worry about anything,' Amanda whispered back, a little breathless.

Mrs Chandler stretched out a hand and Amanda put hers in it. 'Promise me you'll stay until I'm well enough to get up again.'

'There's no need to promise. You *know* I will!'

Marc's voice was calm, but there was an undercurrent of feeling in it. 'You're making her commit herself, Mamma!'

'Not only for *me*!' Mrs Chandler said strangely. 'I could never, never trust Caroline with the children.'

'Good God, Mamma, that's our problem, isn't it?'

Marc said with soft exasperation.

'My darling son!'

Marc came to her and held her other hand. 'You're indescribably precious to me. Just get better.'

'I will, dear. Take care of Amanda and she'll take care of the children. Now go, both of you, I'm tired.'

Her eyelids drooped and almost on cue Nurse Mellon tapped on the door, then entered, bringing with her Mrs Chandler's evening medication. 'I think your mother should rest now, Mr Chandler.'

'Yes.' His black eyes glittered under the lids. You'll wake me immediately should I be needed?'

Nurse Mellon held the glass of water and the capsule in her hand. 'I'm hoping she will have a peaceful night, but of course I'll let you know otherwise.' The dull grey eyes flickered over Amanda, then back to the hard, handsome man who was making her Miss Caroline so unhappy.

'And my wife?' he asked.

'Sleeping quietly. I had to give her a sedative, she was so dreadfully upset.'

At that old Mrs Chandler's eyelids fluttered, but her son said nothing, his face cold and fastidious.

'Goodnight, then.'

'Goodnight Mr Chandler. Miss Raymond.'

Amanda only nodded, her eyes on the frail figure in the bed. Seemingly unaccountably Mrs Chandler had placed all her trust in her and she was determined to keep her free of all anxiety until she was well again.

Marc put his hand on her shoulder, guiding her to the door. For an instant as he turned to gaze back at his mother, his hand gripped tightly on Amanda's delicate shoulder and she felt the tension and anxiety in him. Mrs Chandler lifted a pale hand and smiled and Amanda smiled back, shadows under her cheekbones, her eyes a sparkling, pure green, her hair curving in a silver-gilt stream over Marc's hand. Nurse Mellon beside the bed gave them a hard, watchful look, then she turned back to her patient, her expression softening as she scanned the narrow outline of the old lady's body.

'Feeling better?' she asked.

'Much, much better, thank God!'

Marc shut the door, his dark face baffled and angry as though all his plans had boomeranged on him.

'If she dies. . . .'

'She's not going to!' Despite herself Amanda rested her hand on his arm, feeling the heat of his skin.

His black brows drew together and he looked down at her tender, deeply feminine face. 'I'm going out again,' he said gruffly.

'Where?'

'It would be so easy to take you.'

His voice flicked her like a whip, the powerful vitality that nothing seemed to quench. 'Then you don't know me at all.'

'Don't I?' There was a barbed note in his voice.

She drew in her breath, unbearably aware of him. 'I'll say goodnight, Mr Chandler. I've promised your mother I'll stay until she's fit again and I'm not going to let you make things hard for me!'

The air was electric and she spun on her heel, making off along the corridor as though the very Prince of Darkness was after her. She had missed dinner, but she wasn't hungry. What she wanted was her bed. Her own bed, all alone, not almost drowning in a man's brilliant eyes. It would be better, much better, when she met the young Mrs Chandler and this whole seething world of emotion was brought to an abrupt halt. Marc Chandler was married. Happy or unhappy, he belonged to another woman and she wasn't going to forget it. Neither was he, she was forced to concede that even if she wished he hadn't put it so brutally. This was a dark fantasy and she had to break out of it. Some time tomorrow she would ring Rob. Rob didn't inspire shattering, never-to-be-borne excitement, but he cared for her, and he had a right to.

CHAPTER SIX

KARIN had such a disturbed night, Amanda was forced to take the child into her bed to calm her. Karin was, Amanda realised, a very disturbed child altogether and perhaps she was foolish in wishing she could work a miracle with her small charge. Karin had a mother and father when she herself had been orphaned so early. But there had been peace and laughter with her dear aunt, loving arms to hold her close. It grieved her to think such things weren't taken for granted in Karin's young life, and Karin herself had given Amanda the clue to her mother's personality. There could scarcely be a child alive who wouldn't exchange beauty for niceness. That was what being a mother was all about, having the tenderness and strength to inspire trust and a deep fulfilling love.

Karin had talked and trembled for more than an hour, then she had fallen off to sleep leaving Amanda staring into the darkness, haunted by what the child had said. Finally, out of pure weariness, she too had fallen asleep and neither of them stirred until the door of Amanda's bedroom burst open shortly before seven the next morning. Amanda came awake instantly, rising up swiftly and reaching for her robe.

Morning sunlight drenched her in its dazzling beauty, pointing up the flawless young skin, the slender girl's body, the shining fall of ash-gold hair. A woman stood there staring at her, imperious and arrogant, moved to frantic rage.

'How *dare* you!' she snapped, and rushed across the bedroom to the still drowsy, bewildered child. 'What are you doing here, Karin?' She put out her thin arms to grasp the child and Karin immediately began struggling.

'Mrs Chandler!' Amanda exclaimed, holding her voice down to calmness. 'Karin had a nightmare and she couldn't sleep.'

'Don't speak to me!' Caroline almost shrieked, while Karin pushed her mother off, leaping off the bed and demanding Amanda's protection.

'How *dare* you take my child! How *dare* you cause me a moment's anxiety!'

'I'm so sorry!' Amanda was almost overwhelmed by the terrible tone, the crimson spots of colour in the pale cheeks, the light glittering eyes. 'Karin needed comforting and I was awake.'

Caroline was still staring at her wildly. 'I've seen you before, haven't I?'

'Doctor McGilvray thought I might be able to help you with the children,' Amanda offered steadily.

Caroline laughed and incredibly her eyes swam with tears. 'You're trying to take her from me, aren't you?'

'*No!*' Amanda protested. 'How could I?'

'Marc brought you here, didn't he?' Caroline asked triumphantly. 'He wouldn't care how he hurts me. He gives orders all the time and everyone obeys.'

Amanda could have wept for her, she looked so brittle and bitter, her cloudy blue peignoir falling away from the exquisite matching nightgown to reveal the extreme thinness of the body beneath.

'Mrs Elizabeth Chandler asked me to stay,' Amanda said with such an unmistakable ring of truth that Caroline frowned, drawing the butterfly brows together over her light, shining eyes.

'Not Marc?' she faltered.

'I don't believe Mr Chandler wants me to remain more than a few days, or at least until his mother is better.'

'This child nearly killed her!' Caroline looked down at her daughter with awful, accusing eyes.

'That's not true at all!' Amanda said swiftly, trying to keep the shock out of her voice.

'How do you know, you weren't there!'

'Don't, Mummy! I've said I'm truly sorry!' Karin spun about and buried her head against Amanda's side while Amanda clasped the child firmly, looking across at the beautiful, gaunt woman who was Karin's mother.

'Show a little mercy!' she begged in a saddened rush.

'Mercy—my God!' Caroline's voice rose shrilly, the nervous tenseness of her body suggesting her sufferings were great. 'Does anyone show mercy to *me*?'

Amanda looked back at her mutely. From intuition and experience she knew Caroline was genuinely tormented, yet she was deriving a curious enjoyment from her performance, like a great actress feeling herself into a role.

'Why don't you go and see if Pip's awake?' Amanda said to the apprehensive child, forcing her voice to a natural tone.

'She'll stay *right here*!' Caroline ordered, and that was enough for her small daughter. Karin half turned her head to glimpse her mother's face, then she instantly turned it back into Amanda's side, seeming to choke a little.

'Can't we speak about this, Mrs Chandler, when Karin's not here?'

Caroline said nothing, her strange eyes on Amanda's face. She wore no make-up at that time of the morning and her skin was a deadly white. There was something horribly disconcerting about that stare, an insistence that wasn't normal.

'*Mrs Chandler?*' It broke from Amanda involuntarily, the kind of tone she used at the Centre when something was happening to one of the patients.

Caroline's gaze broke and slid to the quivering child. 'This child will be the death of me! Don't be deceived by the way she's acting now. She's a little hellion!'

Amanda's green eyes challenged Mrs Chandler's basilisk stare. 'If I'm going to look after her, I'd like to discuss her little problems in private. Can't you see she's shaking and frightened?'

'As well she might be!' Caroline returned curtly, 'and believe me, whoever you are, you won't be staying!'

A cry broke from Karin that turned Amanda's heart over. She wished she was strong enough to pick the child up bodily and rush her out of the room, but she had to get past Caroline, and Caroline, she knew, was strong enough and frantic enough to prevent her.

'Come away from there, Karin!' Caroline demanded, advancing on them both like a stalking animal.

Amanda felt every muscle in her body tensing. 'Until I'm told differently by Mr Chandler, Karin remains in my care.'

'Of course!' Caroline stopped short and said in a high, strained voice, 'It's Marc all along. He picked you out, didn't he? You're involved with him?'

'My involvement is with Karin!' Amanda contradicted, standing stock still. 'And I intend to do my best with her.'

Karin's speechless, trembling presence gave Amanda all the courage she needed. Under no circumstances was she going to hand the child over to her mother now. It was obvious that in her present mood Caroline filled her small daughter with fear.

'You mean you're defying me in my own home?' Caroline asked slowly, her thin body tense as if it was about to spring.

'I'm not defying you, Mrs Chandler,' Amanda returned quietly, holding the livid eyes. 'I'm only trying to think what's best for Karin.'

'You ... *you*....'

Amanda recoiled, but she still held the child. Exactly at that moment Nurse Mellon came through the door in an explosive rush calling Caroline's name. '*Miss Caroline!*'

Caroline whirled, lips parted and cried out piteously, 'She's keeping my child from me!'

'We'll see about that!' Nurse Mellon declared. 'Don't you go upsetting yourself, I'll attend to this. Now then, young lady,' she spoke firmly to Karin's back, 'come here to your mother!'

Karin went limp and Amanda immediately banished all her own fears. 'Keep out of this, Nurse!' she said with considerable sharpness and a hard look of disapproval. 'Karin is *my* charge!'

Nurse Mellon shook her head in utter disbelief. 'You have a nerve!'

'Go on, get out of this room!'

'The temerity!' Nurse Mellon stuttered, the wind

seemingly taken right out of her sails. She glanced at the silent Caroline for support, but Caroline was looking ghastly.

'Mrs Chandler doesn't seem well,' Amanda pointed out. 'I'm sorry this had to happen, especially with Karin barely awake, but now is not the right time to talk. I'm prepared to speak to Mrs Chandler alone, any time she wishes.'

'What a very odd girl you are!' Caroline announced unexpectedly. 'Quite the oddest person I've ever met!'

Nurse Mellon went to her and made soothing noises. 'She'll be gone by this evening!'

'You're giving orders around here, are you, Nurse?'

Shock robbed Nurse Mellon of all her protective fire. She spun around to see Marc Chandler standing at the door, his expression one of cold, merciless autocracy.

'I beg your pardon, Mr Chandler, but this young woman has been thoroughly upsetting your wife!'

'A lot *he'd* care!' Caroline found her voice.

Marc Chandler moved into the room, a tall, powerful man, supremely sure of himself and not kind. 'I suggest we allow Miss Raymond the privacy of her bedroom. I feel somewhat to blame, I didn't prepare her for the likelihood of these early morning disturbances.' His black eyes just briefly touched Amanda's face and shaking body, then he reached past her and scooped Karin up into his arms.

'Daddy has to go to work now. Pip is still asleep. You go and curl up quietly beside him until Amanda comes to get you. She's staying to look after you and I'm going to put a car at her disposal. It's just the right day for a picnic and when I come home I'm sure you'll have lots to tell me.'

'I love you!' Karin said in a shaky, breath punctu-ated whisper.

'Keep loving me, baby!' he said, and lowered her to the floor. 'Go through the side door.'

'Yes, Daddy.'

Karin stumbled away, a small figure in a flower-sprigged nightgown, and Amanda felt sick with com-passion. She looked at Marc Chandler, clear-eyed and alert, conscious that she was in her thin nightclothes but sobered by his hard, controlled expression.

'Before you go, Mr Chandler, would you make it quite clear that if I'm to help Karin we can't have these showdowns?'

Caroline laughed violently, her blue eyes devouring her husband. 'You heard her, forbid me to see my own child!'

Amanda swallowed. 'I only mean, Mrs Chandler, that I can't have Nurse Mellon's interference or scenes in front of the children.'

Nurse Mellon raised a shocked, resentful face. 'Be-lieve me, Mr Chandler, I was acting for the best. This young woman here—you never *heard* her—was speak-ing most disrespectfully to Mrs Chandler. I couldn't allow it!'

'Naturally not!' Marc returned suavely. 'You're sure under the circumstances you wish to stay?'

Nurse Mellon expelled a breath and anxiety rushed into her dull grey eyes. 'Mrs Chandler needs me,' she insisted.

'My mother?'

'Of course, sir. Miss Caroline too. After all, I was hired to look after her.'

'Then surely you can best do that by anticipating these disturbances?'

Caroline's thin body jerked all over. 'I missed her. I looked in her room, but she was gone. What does each day mean but worse terror? She could have gone down to the river and drowned!'

'*No!*' Marc Chandler said simply. 'Maybe while you're here, Amanda, you could teach Karin to swim. Pip can, of course, my sister's household is quite different from this.'

'I won't have it!' Caroline burst out, white-lipped.

'I have to draw the line at that particular fear,' her husband said harshly. 'The only way to prevent drowning accidents is to teach all children to swim, the sooner the better. You've terrified Karin enough on that score. As you've pointed out yourself, it could cost her her life. I'm sorry you weren't well enough to meet Amanda yesterday, but she's here to stay for some weeks at least.'

A stifled sound of distress broke from Caroline. 'You've already made up your mind?'

'I have,' Marc said with finality. 'You're excused, Nurse. I'm sure you want to look in on my mother.'

'Certainly, sir,' Nurse Mellon returned quietly, and made towards the door.

'Be warned, Nurse!' Marc Chandler's voice stopped her. 'I won't have my mother disturbed,' he said distinctly. 'You have your duties and I'm relying on you to perform them well. Miss Raymond is in charge of the children, sole charge, and answerable to me. If there is anything that bothers you feel free to come and speak to me about it. Doctor McGilvray will be looking in some time today and if you need me ring my secretary. She'll find me wherever I am.'

'Very good, sir.' Nurse Mellon made straight through the door, her expression frigidly professional.

'Shall we leave too, Caroline?' Marc Chandler said crisply, and glanced at his wife.

'How can I?' Caroline's voice soared.

'Well, I must go,' he shrugged, reaching out and grasping her arm, 'and you have to come with me.'

'Don't think I can't guess!' Caroline snapped, and her voice was like splintering glass. 'Have you ever kissed her until her mind reels and her body does whatever you wish it?'

'Sorry,' he said curtly, 'I don't even dare to think of it. I'll never leave you, Caroline.'

'You *want* to!' Caroline seemed much quieter now, pathetically grateful for the arm her unsmiling husband put around her slight shoulders.

'I remember too well how many times I've told you. I don't want to start telling you again. I'll never leave you, *ever*. You're my wife, my responsibility.'

'People are always talking,' Caroline murmured, and gave a long, luxurious sigh.

'Let them.'

'Oh, Amanda!' Caroline tilted her head back and incredibly she was smiling, dangerous no longer, supported by her husband. 'Forgive that ghastly little scene this morning. I'm just such an anxious mother it shocked me to find Karin missing from her bed.'

'I understand, Mrs Chandler,' Amanda said politely, feeling quite unreal.

'Can I come on your picnic?' Caroline added. 'I want to.'

'Aren't you having your hair done?' Marc Chandler commented. 'I'm expected to entertain Senator Bradford and his party. They're flying in this afternoon.'

'You're still proud of me—as your wife?' Caroline looked up at him shakily.

'You're a very beautiful woman.'

'Yes, I am!' Caroline retorted on a note of pure pleasure. 'I'm sorry, Amanda, you'll have to take the children without me.'

'Perhaps another day,' said Amanda, and Caroline nodded.

'That will be nice.'

'Can you drive?' Marc Chandler looked over his wife's dark head with his curious lancing gaze.

'Yes,' Amanda returned quietly, 'I have a licence. We did have a car, but it proved rather a luxury and I had to let it go.'

'I'll have one delivered this morning. One you can handle!'

'Thank you!' she said a shade dryly, wondering if there was a man alive who didn't think women and motor cars didn't really mix.

He smiled suddenly as if reading her thoughts, and she only wished he would go. Smiling, his dark formidable face had a dark fascination that could never be for her. She turned her blonde head with a funny little dismissive gesture of her own and when she turned it back again, they had gone.

Realising how shaky she was, Amanda moved closer to an armchair and sat down. Up until now she had thought Marc Chandler a hard, exciting man; a man of contradictions, tender to his small daughter, cruel perhaps to his wife. Now she knew he was holding tenaciously to his marriage. Whether as a man of honour or whether the flame of love remained, she would never know. She was too young, too inexperienced to know the vagaries of the human heart. It was none of her concern anyway and the terrible meaning of her own racing pulses had to be forgotten.

The only thing of which she was certain was that she couldn't abandon Karin now. Time enough for that when old Mrs Chandler was better and she had had a little space to work a small miracle like stabilising a highly strung child completely in the grip of her mother's unpredictable behaviour. Only a fool would have imagined it was going to be easy, and Amanda was no fool. The thing to do was to start out as she meant to go on. A picnic today, a little much-needed relaxation for the over-strung Karin, then tomorrow a time-table had to be drawn up. Hours for lessons, and now that she had approval from Marc Chandler she would begin to teach Karin to swim.

All the child's fears seemed to have been implanted by her mother, and Amanda wondered whether Caroline had suffered some traumatic experience that made her frightened of the water and unwilling to allow her small daughter to go near it. Living as they did on the river, with a magnificent pool set like a jewel in the beautifully landscaped grounds, it was a state of affairs that couldn't be allowed to continue. If she handled Karin well with understanding and confidence all would be well. Pip would be a great help. Dear little Pip, with his gentle loving understanding and his brilliant laughter-filled brown eyes.

Thinking of the children, Amanda got to her feet. There were things to be done on the instant and she was a governess with limited powers. She would wash and dress, then supervise the children's dressing before they all went down to breakfast. Then, if the children's grandmother was sufficiently improved for her peace of mind, they would spend the day at the lake and the bird sanctuary. She had always loved it as a child.

The dinner party Amanda heard about afterwards in detail, first from Brenda who liked nothing better than a gossip, then from Mrs Harper who was understandably proud that the Senator had called for her to congratulate her on such a 'splendid repast' complete with 'bravos'. The afternoon had been spent at the mine watching the giant power shovels load the big boulders of ore into the waiting trucks for transport to the mill where the ore was crushed, the waste rock removed and the resulting mixture smelted down to metallic copper. A great percentage of the copper produced at Mount Regina was used by the electrical industry and one of the members of the party was from a government authority. Amanda had only seen over the mine once as a schoolgirl on a conducted tour, but along with most of her friends she had become interested in copper work and she still had a few of the pieces she had hammered into decorative and unusual dishes and jewellery.

Young Mrs Chandler, reportedly, had looked radiant, 'more like her old self', and Amanda concluded correctly that she had extraordinary, recuperative powers. They were essential in Chandler's first lady, for now it was Christmas week and the phone rang most of the day and well into the evening.

In keeping with the general festive feeling, Amanda didn't keep Karin to lessons beyond an hour or so in the morning, but when the holiday season was over,

Karin would have to settle down and pay attention if she wanted to keep pace with her classmates. Karin was, as Amanda suspected, highly intelligent and knowing, but she had very little concentration and a marked contempt for anything arithmetical. Pip, in fact, two years her junior, could solve all the little sums Amanda set his cousin, demonstrating his own precocity in that direction and inflaming Karin to start out on a tantrum that both Pip and Amanda sensibly ignored. Without the promise of an anguished audience, Karin was often forced to abandon a spectacular display of temperament and behave like a reasonable little human being. When she did, she was charming, but there were still odd occasions when she became obstinate and resentful and she had so far declined a swimming lesson. Amanda, sensing her fear, didn't push the child, but she and Pip swam daily and Karin was coming closer and closer to the water of her own accord.

Functions came and went and Amanda wasn't included in any of them, nor did she expect to be. Old Mrs Chandler was improving in health and seemingly in her reduced state dependent on Amanda's daily visits with the children and the hurried little consultations they managed until Nurse Mellon found some reason to look in on her patient. Karin, according to the staff, was behaving in an unprecedentedly angelic fashion, and Amanda was content with that. So too was her grandmother, who got up briefly one day to see the giant tapering tree Amanda and the children had decorated.

Of Marc, Amanda saw little, indeed she was certain he was avoiding her when she desperately wished he wouldn't put himself to the bother. Her whole mind was given over to the children, but it was almost fun to watch Caroline dashing in and out of the house, always fabulously dressed, followed by Lee staggering under the weight of parcels wrapped in gay Christmas paper and beautifully decorated boxes fixed with ribbons and baubles.

Then it was Christmas Eve and Rob invited Amanda out to a party. She was mildly surprised to hear from him because he had been violently outspoken about her position in the Chandler household. Rob with very little encouragement was too possessive altogether, but it was a relief to be invited out when there was going to be a big party at the house.

With her comparatively lavish salary as the Chandler governess Amanda bought herself a party dress, wryly admitting to herself that she had been stirred into it by the daily sight of Caroline in her lovely clothes. Not that she could ever look like Caroline with her strange, exotic beauty, she was just Amanda, or Mandy as the children now called her. Still, the dress was very pretty and when she had taken a last look in the mirror she went into the sitting room where the children were watching television to keep the promise she had made them.

'They looked up together, their small faces shining.

'You look beautiful!' they both exclaimed together. Pip without any qualification and Karin eyeing Amanda critically up and down.

'I wish you could wear some of Mummy's jewels. She has far too many—not that that little chain doesn't look pretty!'

'I like you just the way you are,' Pip said stoutly, offering reassurance. 'Who cares about silly jewels?'

'Not little boys, that's for sure!' Karin sounded sarcastic. She sprang out of her chair and picked up a fold of Amanda's dress. 'This is dreamy! I love you in floaty dresses. You should have a flower in your hair.'

'I'll get you one!' Pip offered eagerly.

'Not now, darling!' Amanda said, and laughed. 'All the guests will be arriving for the party!'

'And why aren't *you* going?' Karin asked for perhaps the twentieth time.

'I *told* you!' Amanda turned back from whirling for Pip's benefit to pat Karin's cheek. 'I'm staff, I work here. These are all Mummy's and Daddy's friends.'

'I thought it was pretty funny myself.' Pip went so far as to turn off the television so he could better take part in the discussion. 'I'm surprised you don't mind.'

'Well, I don't!' Amanda said lightly. 'Up, up, up! You promised me you'd go to bed early because you'll have a big day tomorrow.'

'You bet!' Pip said with bright expectant eyes. 'Mummy and Daddy left all my presents with Uncle Marc and they're going to ring me from wherever they are even if it's the North Pole!'

'Idiot!' jeered Karin. 'You know perfectly well they're in Italy!'

'It will be lovely to hear them, won't it, dear?' Amanda smiled into the beautiful brown eyes, absurdly shaken by Pip's resemblance to his Uncle Marc.

'Next time they promised to take me when my bronchitis clears up.'

'Lovely! Now I have to leave, so into bed with you. Pip, we'll tuck you in first. Then Karin!'

Later, when she walked down the stairway, Rob was

already there, in animated conversation with Caroline.

He stopped when he saw Amanda, his eyes appraising her with complete admiration and a revealing infatuation so that Caroline too had to turn to observe her.

'Oh, there you are, Amanda. How nice you look!' It was said very sweetly, yet suddenly Amanda felt less sure of herself. Caroline's white body was covered by a slender jersey sheath, black touched with crimson at the tightly laced up bodice, and her necklace and matching pendant earrings flashed out fire in the soft dazzle from the overhead chandelier. She looked wonderfully dramatic, and very confident in the way beautiful rich women are always confident.

Amanda didn't answer, but she smiled at both of them. There was the sound of cars coming up the driveway and voices from outside in the garden. Rob was still staring at Amanda with utter admiration, which Amanda thought rather odd considering she was now standing beside Caroline, when Caroline suddenly grasped Rob's arm.

'You mustn't go away and leave us. I mean, you just *mustn't*! I'm sure if you ask Amanda very nicely, she'll consent to stay.'

Amanda could scarcely point out that she had never been invited, but from the look on Rob's face he obviously thought it was a splendid idea. 'How very kind of you, Mrs Chandler!'

'Actually the party needs another good-looking young man!' Caroline smiled at Rob, establishing a warm intimacy, then she gave Amanda a brief, gleaming glance. '*Do* stay, Amanda, it will make me happy if you do!'

It simply wasn't true. Or was it? Caroline Chandler was a very strange woman and something about her made Amanda feel distinctly uneasy. 'It's very kind of you, Mrs Chandler,' Amanda repeated Rob's very words, 'but we're expected at another party, aren't we, Rob?'

'Nothing we can't get out of,' said Rob, the indefatigable social climber. 'Relax, Mandy. I'm sure Mrs Chandler won't mind if I give my friends a ring. They'll understand perfectly.'

'Go right ahead!' Caroline said gaily. 'Use the library extension, then you won't be disturbed. Amanda will show you.'

'Thank you!' Rob took Amanda's arm and she could sense the excitement in him.

'It's through this way,' she said rather coolly.

'*Darling!*' He glanced down at her beautiful, shining head, brushed into a faultless silky slide.

'I don't think I'd understand if I was the friend giving the party!' she added.

'But then you're a proper little thing! They won't mind, believe me, particularly when I tell them I've been invited to the Big House.'

'A last-minute invitation?' Amanda said bluntly.

'What's wrong with that?' Rob smiled at her, looking very suave and handsome in his evening clothes. 'One must grasp one's opportunities. I mean, you did, didn't you, darling!'

She drew away from him and he immediately apologised. 'I'm sorry, Mandy! I've been storing up the thought of seeing you all day long, don't let's spoil it all by arguing. You look beautiful, like spring, and your eyes are as green as the leaves on your dress.' His eyes slipped over her face and body, touching her throat, the girl's breasts, the lovely long line of her. 'That's a very pretty dress—very feminine!'

'It cost rather a lot!' She held her voice to lightness.

'And you planned it all for me?'

She recognised the faint malice in his voice and went ahead quickly to the library, switching on the light.

Rob followed her, whistling gently as he gazed about the room. 'All the good things of life! This is some house, isn't it? I mean, you nearly have to turn green with envy.'

'Not me,' Amanda said truthfully. 'Do you know your friends' number?'

Rob merely walked behind the big mahogany desk, smiling largely. 'All my life I've wanted a desk like this.'

'Then why don't you try to get one?'

'Surely one needs a lot of money and the right establishment to put it in. Simmer down, pet, you seem to be looking for a little conflict when all I want is peace. And love!' He looked up smiling, with a certain smugness around his curving mouth.

'I'll leave you to it,' said Amanda, realising she didn't want to listen in to his conversation. 'Now that we're staying I'll just have a word with Mrs Chandler.'

'Caro?'

'Mrs *Elizabeth* Chandler!' Amanda corrected, almost gratefully. From a pleasurable excitement she was fast moving towards an actual unease. Just a few moments in Mrs Chandler's company would calm her. She hadn't felt up to any parties, but she would probably be reading in her room. Nurse Mellon, mercifully, had been given time off to visit her only remaining relative, a widowed sister. Amanda wasn't in the least concerned about leaving Rob on his own for a while. He was sleek and smart enough to look after himself.

Outside Mrs Chandler's bedroom door, she tapped softly, hearing the calm, mellow voice calling:

'Come in!'

She entered at once, a smile on her mouth that faltered as she saw Marc Chandler leaning over his mother's bed. His face in the lamplight was all angled planes and shadows, the cleft in his chin very deep. She could never, *never* be immune to him no matter how hard she tried. His brilliant black eyes locked her to him across the intervening space and just for a second she caught a glimmer of some emotion in his eyes. Then he straightened and there was a hard mocking quality to his voice.

'Well, well, little Amanda, about to go out for the night?'

How easily he hurt her! She tilted her head back, looking almost ethereal against the dark, glowing panelling of the door. 'I just wanted to say goodnight to Mrs Chandler.'

'Isn't *she* lucky! Come over here, Amanda, I won't bite you!'

'*Marc!*' Mrs Chandler's voice was quiet but implacable. She gestured to Amanda to come nearer the bed, her dark eyes smiling, her silver-grey hair still fastidiously groomed for all her undeniably frailer appearance. 'What a nice child you are, Amanda, and how lovely you look. What's the matter?'

'Maybe she's in love!' said Marc like a barb to taunt her. 'Hasn't Courtney arrived yet?'

'Oh yes!' Amanda lifted her shining head.

'Well?' His smile hardened, while his mother looked from one to the other.

'You should have been there!' Amanda answered, sounding faintly harassed. 'Mrs Chandler invited us to the party!'

'Really?' he said grimly.

'She should have done that ages ago!' his mother said firmly. 'Go and enjoy yourself, Amanda.'

She tried to speak and realised she was incredibly near tears. 'I ... I ... just don't know!'

'Nonsense!' Elizabeth Chandler caught her hand and pressed it. 'Do you think it's some kind of a cruel joke, child?'

Colour raced up under her pearly skin. 'No, of course not!' she protested, unwilling to cause Marc's mother the slightest anxiety.

'Then why are your eyes shimmering with tears?' Marc demanded, so darkly, vividly handsome that unaccountably she hated him.

'They are *not*!' She stared back at him with a jewelled flash of anger, a lovely wild rose flush over her cheekbones. 'What a terrible son you have, Mrs Chandler!'

'I know,' Elizabeth Chandler returned steadily, 'but I love him and I only want him to be happy.'

'He doesn't look happy!' Amanda said like an over-wrought child.

'What else is new?' Marc asked a shade caustically, then he bent over and kissed his mother's cheek. 'Goodnight, Mamma. Sleep well.'

'Goodnight, darling.' She lifted one hand and stroked back the thick, closely curling black hair.

'Goodnight, Mrs Chandler,' Amanda said with sweet

sincerity. 'Thank you for always being so kind to me.'

'My dear child!' Mrs Chandler said with surprise. 'It's you that's making my progress so much easier. You're a really good girl!'

'No one is going to argue with that,' Marc murmured mockingly. 'Come along, little one, if you must go to the party, let's go!'

'Bless you both!' Elizabeth Chandler lifted a hand and smiled, lying back very quiet and peaceful in the queen-sized canopied bed.

Outside in the softly lit corridor Amanda was driven to saying: 'I'm sorry if you didn't want me to come to the party.'

'No need to cry about it!' His arrogant glance struck her face and her creamy sloping shoulders, as if the very sight of her was feeding his anger.

'I just want you to know I didn't want to come either.'

'Well, that's only being smart!' he shrugged, his black eyes narrowing. 'Just keep as far away from me as you can!'

Amanda could feel herself go white, even sway, and he reached for her suddenly, closing his hands over the delicate bones of her shoulders. 'Stop that!'

She made a small sound of pain and closed her eyes. 'I hate it when you're so cruel. It's so unnecessary!'

'*Is* it?' he said tautly, hurting her so she had to put up a hand to ease his hard, biting fingers.

'I'm fine!' she said untruthfully. 'I won't even look in your direction, I promise.'

'Oh, *please*!' he said in a moody voice that tore at her. 'I'm surprised Courtney wants to mingle with my friends when he finds you on your own so desirable.'

'You make it sound strange!' she said with brittle irony, and moved away from him.

'What, that he wants you very badly?'

'That's my affair,' she said with a kind of recklessness,' and not for you to approve or disapprove.'

'And why should I give a damn?' he asked unpleasantly.

She swallowed convulsively, frighteningly aware of the anger or antagonism between them. 'I'm ready to leave this house whenever you say the word.' Her blonde head was thrown back, gleaming in the pool of light from the wall bracket.

'What when you've made yourself practically indispensable?' His brilliant glance sharpened over her, a biting sardonic note in his voice.

'Not at all!' Amanda gave a little negating shake of her head.

'But I don't want to. *Yet!*' he said tautly. 'I feel bound to tell you, Amanda, that I'm deeply grateful for the way you're handling the children and bringing a measure of peace to my mother. We must have a good long talk about it some time, when you're feeling more normal.'

There was no way she could answer his arrogance. In any case, she was shaking when he was thoroughly controlled.

'You'll excuse me?' she asked, trying to keep the intense hurt out of her voice.

'I'll be glad to,' he said jarringly.

Amanda waited for no more. She fled along the corridor and down the stairs where Rob with his heart-warming admiration was waiting for her anxiously.

CHAPTER SEVEN

AMANDA awoke early Christmas morning after a few hours of helpless, bitter dreams in which Marc Chandler figured largely. The party had been a very disillusioning affair for her at least, because Caroline had used the glittering occasion to subtly humiliate her in every way she could, bringing to everyone's attention Amanda's true status in the house, that of a lowly employee. Not that many of the guests seemed to mind. Any girl as beautiful and gentle as Amanda could find herself friends, and Marc Chandler's Uncle Clive and his wife had been particularly gracious, going out of their way to offset the effect of Caroline's seemingly casual and innocent little taunts.

Almost too late, Rob had begun to understand what was happening, the vindictiveness behind Caroline's brilliant, empty smiles, so that his evening too had been spoilt, leaving a bitter aftertaste. In the moment when he had taken Amanda into his arms and kissed her goodnight he told her quite brutally that her self-preservation instinct wasn't functioning properly. Caroline Chandler in his opinion was a threatening kind of woman for all her enthralling icy beauty and she was mad about her husband, whether in love or in hate.

Inertly Amanda lay in her great fourposter bed looking up at the rose-coloured canopy embellished with a pattern of flower-studded vines. A large gilt mirror set into the wall gave back her reflection. She looked pale, green eyes shadowed, a different girl from the one who had come into this house not a few weeks before. No matter how much she was helping Karin and taking some of the burden of anxiety from old Mrs Chandler she would have to go. She hadn't even been tempted to look in Marc's direction right through the long party, but even the thought of him was complicating her life unbearably. She struggled against the memory of the few moments she had spent alone with him last night, but it came near to submerging her. Asleep and awake he seemed to defeat her. Then, because she was ashamed, she turned and buried her aching head in the pillows, limp as a rag doll but too conscious of the hot blood beating through her body.

Even as she lay there, with scarcely a sound to alert her, the children slipped into the room, staring at her buried head, then when they saw it move, they rushed her with laughter and excited:

'Happy Christmas, Mandy!'

'Happy Christmas!'

She rolled over and they leapt on to the bed like puppies. 'Tell us about the party!'

'You're tired!' remarked the observant Pip. 'I can see it in your face.'

'I am a little, darling, but never mind. I've got something for you both.'

'Oh, really?' Karin slid her arms around Amanda's shoulders and kissed her. 'So have we. Got presents for you, I mean, but they're under the tree.'

'That was very sweet of you. You'll find yours in the walk-in wardrobes in your rooms.'

'Oh, beaut, a treasure trove!'

Both children were off and Amanda slid wearily out of the bed, pulling on her robe. A glance at the bed-side clock told her it was barely six—not that she could sleep anyway. Inevitably her thoughts turned back to the last Christmas she had spent with her aunt, and she had a sudden attack of utter loneliness. Of course Christmas was for families, and she had no one at all. Even Rob was flying down to the State capital to spend two days with his parents. He had invited her, concerned that she would be lonely and unhappy with the magnificent portals of the Chandler mansion, and it seemed now he would be right. Still, she hadn't wanted to intrude on the Courtneys' private family gathering, nor did she want Rob to become more possessive of her than he already was.

The children came rushing back into the room, struggling with ribbons, and Amanda sank back on to the bed again, eased and comforted by their innocent pleasure and excitement. She hadn't been able to buy either of them anything grand, but their faces told her what she had decided on was priceless. Pip clutched his airport crash truck, exclaiming over it, and Karin looked at her wide-eyed before she slipped on a charming little silver bracelet with an ornamental silver heart attached to it with her name on it. Then both of them came to her, kissing a cheek each resoundingly. It seemed to Amanda then that that was what Christmas was all about; sacrifices all over the world to make children glad.

Half way through the morning, with the children playing happily with a veritable Aladdin's cave of toys, Marc Chandler came into the sitting room to talk to her. They had met at breakfast, a meal made easy by the children's laughter and excitement and it was to be admitted Caroline's absence, and afterwards Karin had presented her with a present 'from all of us', thrusting it into Amanda's hands, her eyes pleading with her to open it just as quickly as she could. She was wearing it now—a very elegant, expensive, oval-face watch rimmed with gold on a brown crocodile strap. She didn't dare think about how much it had cost, but money wasn't the problem in the Chandler house.

Marc stood there, half smiling, half serious, looking down at the children, then his eyes found Amanda's.

'You didn't sleep, did you?' he asked.

'Does it show so badly?'

'I wish every woman looked like you first thing in the morning. What time was it when you woke me?'

'Not so bad!' she smiled at him. 'Six-thirty. I couldn't hold them after that!'

'All right, Daddy?' Karin lifted her proud little head to smile at him.

'Perfect!' he smiled back, and bowed in her direction.

She laughed happily and returned to the game, and Amanda realised she hadn't asked once after her mother. Caroline, Amanda learned, was sleeping and not to be disturbed. It was no secret either that Marc and his wife didn't share a room, though all the main bedrooms were in the west wing.

'What did you particularly want to do today?' Marc was asking her, releasing her from the gravity of her thoughts.

'Me?' Her wide green eyes looked soft and bewildered.

'Yes, you, Green Eyes!' He was looking very handsome and relaxed in his cool casual clothes, free of the deadly tension that had caught them up so recently.

'Well, I'm happy to do whatever you want to do. I mean, it's a family day, isn't it? The children's day?'

'Be that as it may, I'm going to consider both of us. My wife will sleep through most of the day. She takes no account of the usual festivities and family effort. We may see her before she goes out this evening. She's going to her own family.'

Amanda looked up at him helplessly. 'And will she be taking Karin?'

'No, she will *not* be taking Karin!' he said pointedly. 'Even if she wanted to, which rather pathetically she doesn't. I won't bore you with the complicated details even if you could understand them. No matter what Caroline says, she's not to take Karin out alone.'

'And I'm supposed to stop her?' Despite herself her voice rose sharply.

'Of course. Just long enough for me to get home. But don't panic, little one. Caroline is mostly indifferent.' He walked to the big picture window and looked out. 'A nice couple. Now.... My mother has decided she's going over to Clive and Janet's for a few hours. They particularly miss seeing her and she's very fond of them. The outing should do her good—in fact, she's looking forward to it. We don't have Christmas dinner in the middle of the day, it's far too hot, but she tells me she'll be joining us this evening.'

'That's good news!'

He nodded his head, still looking out over the massed display of roses. 'I'll drive her over when she's ready and Clive will drive her back. I've asked them to stay to dinner and they've agreed. My cousin Julian is in Washington. He's a career diplomat and Anne was painting in the Greek islands last time we heard from her, so they're on their own too.'

'I like them,' Amanda said truthfully. 'They were very nice to me last night.'

'I suppose they admired how you handled a difficult situation, among other things!'

She had nothing to say and the pause lengthened, broken only by Pip's triumphant crow of laughter as he won the board game.

'You cheated!' Karin accused.

'No, no!' Amanda glanced sideways, her voice firmly pleasant. 'It's wrong to say that, Karin. You know Pip played well.'

'All right!' Karin agreed almost absently. 'Let's play again. I'll concentrate this time.'

'You'll have weeks to play with that.' Marc glanced down indulgently. 'This morning we're going to drive Gran over to Uncle Clive's. We'll all say hello very nicely, you can collect yet more presents, then we'll drive out to the Crystal Cascades. I'll find a spot we can have all to ourselves and there are some beautiful walks we can go on. Does that suit you?'

'Can we take a picnic lunch?' Karin asked eagerly.

'I should say so. We can't have you going hungry!'

Pip immediately began to put the game away. 'Is it all right if I bring a few toys, Uncle Marc?'

'Just so long as they don't take up the entire boot!'

'Great!' Pip announced happily. 'It's much better going out than sitting around. I'm going to put my togs on!'

Amanda turned into the capable governess. 'I'll

come with you, Pip, and we'll decide on your clothes. You have to look nice if you're calling in on your uncle and aunt.'

'I'll leave you with it,' Marc said a shade dryly. 'I'll tell Mrs Harper what we need and we should be ready to leave within an hour.'

'I don't have to swim if I don't want to, do I, Daddy?' Karin asked, looking rather worried.

He turned back to answer her. 'It would be more fun if you would join us, but you can just sit there and watch if you like. Amanda is going in, aren't you, Amanda?'

'In this heat it would kill me to stay out, but we'll find a nice spot in the shade for you, Karin,' Amanda said with kind concern, holding the child's eyes.

'Better put my swimmers in in case I change my mind,' suggested Karin.

For a second more Marc stood there, a relaxed humour in his face that made Amanda want to cry, then he smiled at her over Karin's silky head and she knew with a great certainty that she loved him.

Afterwards Amanda was to remember that Christmas Day as one of the happiest she had ever known. Perhaps because it was the beginning of so many things and Marc seemed to her for the first time relaxed and untroubled. It was a wonderful day they both shared with the children, their own spirits lifted by the special joy and excitement that all children felt on that day. At Clive Chandler's they had accepted a sherry and a piece of rich spicy fruit cake and afterwards all three, Elizabeth, Janet and Clive, had stood on the covered porch and waved them off. Amanda remembered exactly the expressions on their faces, the revealing affection and the trace of disquiet.

She hadn't wondered at it, it had been inevitable, but Marc all through that long happy day treated her like a young sister, casually gallant, his dark eyes unmoved by the sight of her as a water sprite, sufficiently Big Brother to plonk a hat on her head in case she got sunburnt, his hard hand at her waist while they clambered around the rocks. The sky overhead had been deep blue and fathomless and the sparkling mountain winds blew fresh in from heaven.

It was life. It was living, and she was in love for the first and only time in her life. Karin too had been affected by the warmth and the ease that flowed backwards and forwards between them and in the green, placid lake with its shimmering silver cascades she first entered the water without fear. A day made for happiness, and Amanda accepted it blindly, like a priceless gift laid in her hands. That she was going to have to pay for it didn't seem to matter. She was dazzled by the radiant feelings that invaded her heart, mind and body.

This curious mood of contentment stayed with her all through the week and into the New Year. Caroline too seemed to thrive on the parties and the shopping trips necessary to outfit her and keep her beautiful dark hair immaculately styled, and if she sometimes swayed a little or her voice slurred Nurse Mellon had returned to care for her and see that she remained quiet until it was time for her to get up and dress for the next party. Amanda and the children saw little enough of her, though Amanda was still shocked at the way eight-year-old Karin took this for granted.

She was cheerful and yielding these days and Brenda and Mrs Harper kept telling Amanda what an admirable girl she was coming to stay and bringing such peace and order into their existence. In short, Karin, the *enfant terrible*, had met her match.

With the Christmas-New Year holidays over, Amanda deemed it necessary to bring in a more stringent schedule. Karin was to return to the exclusive St Margaret's school in February and her work wasn't up to the high standard that would be expected of her. Pip, she had soon found out, was no ordinary little boy when it came to lessons. He was positively brilliant for his age, apparently, as his Uncle Marc had been before him, and Karin apparently found his presence soothing, for she worked better when Pip found it within his kind little heart to join her. The worst of the heat was yet to come and the first cyclone of the season had battered the Far North briefly before petering out in the Coral Sea.

Sitting in the schoolroom, Amanda took pity on Karin's vast sigh. 'What is it, darling, are you feeling the heat?'

'I miss Daddy. He's always away early and we never see him for lunch or supper!'

'He's busy, dear, you know that. It must be a great responsibility seeing that the mine and the mill keep up production.'

'I wish he wasn't so important!' Karin persisted, and tears swam into her lustrous eyes.

'There now!' Amanda moved her chair closer and put an arm around the child. 'What can I tempt you with, you've been working very well.'

'What about a swim?' said Pip, the human fish.

'What about it?' seconded Amanda, 'now that you're starting to enjoy yourself.'

'All right,' Karin answered listlessly, and Amanda tipped up the child's chin to stare into her face. Even the air-conditioning was faltering on such a scorching hot day. 'Daddy will be very pleased with your progress and if he's home early enough we'll ask him up to supper.'

'He won't be,' said Karin without any hope at all. 'Even Mr Gerhardt can't manage to see him. I heard Brenda talking on the telephone this morning. A new order is in from Japan and they're blasting another pit.'

'Then we must accept it,' Amanda said philosophically. 'Daddy is a very important and successful man and a lot of people are dependent upon him. I expect he gets tired of the constant pressure on him as well.'

'I'll get your flippers,' Pip offered with his usual consideration.

'My goggles as well!' Karin added pathetically. 'I'll get sore eyes without them.'

In the pool, Amanda and Karin stayed at the shallow end kicking and splashing, the easiest way, Amanda had found, to accustom the fearful Karin to a new environment. After that Amanda put on the child's flippers and with the aid of a kick board Karin was able to move about in the water with some agility, although she refused point blank to put her head under water even with her goggles on. Today for some reason she was more rigid and fearful than ever, though Amanda stood up repeatedly in the water to show how shallow it was. The confident Pip she had almost forgotten until he surfaced beside her.

'Come on, Kat, don't be frightened!' His pleasure in the water was evident and he moved over to the edge of the pool to grasp at the other kick board Uncle Marc had provided. 'Let's practise the right kick. The flippers should make it easy for you.'

'I don't want to!'

'Then let's practise ducking our heads under water. You'll never swim if you don't put your head under water.'

Amanda could see Karin was becoming more difficult and nervous by the minute. She went to grasp the child with an outstretched arm to reassure her when Karin began to scream in earnest, calling the attention of everyone in the house.

'Ah, stop it!' Pip exclaimed in swift disgust.

'Out of the water, Karin!' Amanda ordered firmly, 'seeing you don't feel like it!'

Karin's eyes were glittering behind the goggles and Amanda pulled them off the child's head, telling herself to treat the child calmly. Karin's terrified yells had intensified, although she was now on a shallow step of the pool.

'Karin, what is it?' Amanda looked straight into the staring eyes.

'Get me out of here! I can't stand it!'

'All right then, don't panic, the water is only lapping around your ankles!'

Even as she was soothing the child Caroline Chandler ran frantically along the side of the house followed up by the tall dark man Amanda knew as her cousin Dominic O'Neill. He wasn't such a fool as to come to the house when Marc was home, but Marc was away at the new pit site and well he knew it.

Amanda could feel her own nerve shaken by the sight of Caroline's face. She was pale and sweating and she backed away from the pool, shrilling at Amanda:

'What are you doing?'

She sounded panic-stricken, as if she had found Amanda giving the child mouth-to-mouth resuscitation.

'I'm trying to get Karin out of the water.' Amanda's eyes fell on Dominic O'Neill and she looked away again. He was still, so still, staring at her.

'You had to do this to her, didn't you?' Caroline's voice continued to soar. 'You and Marc between you. There's no change in her. She's terrified!'

Oddly Karin had lost all desire to yell and was now clutching at Amanda's shoulder.

'You've got a lot to answer for, frightening my child!'

Amanda mastered her anger, drawing herself and the unprotesting Karin right out of the pool, standing on the tiled surround in full view of Dominic O'Neill's shivery stare. 'If you don't mind, Mrs Chandler, I'll take Karin into the house. She really is improving, you know. This was simply a little setback.'

Caroline gave her strange high-pitched laugh again. 'You see what they're doing, Dom?'

With one hand Dominic O'Neill reached out and touched Amanda's long wet hair and she drew back from him abruptly. 'Excuse me!'

Although he was a very lean man in a faultless casual jacket and narrow trousers there was a grossness, an animality about him that set her seething with disapproval. How did his cousin Caroline interpret his naked glance? But Caroline wasn't even looking at him, glaring at Amanda as if the sight of her flared her into an intolerable rage.

By a miracle Karin had quietened, leaving the hysterics to her mother. Amanda scarcely heard what Caroline screamed after her, as she shepherded the two children ahead of her. Karin began to weep quietly and in all her life Amanda hadn't heard a more desolate sound.

'It's all right, dear, believe me. No one is angry!'

Glancing sideways, Pip delivered his opinion. 'Boy, can Aunt Caroline scream! What was she screaming about anyway?'

'She wants me to drown!' shuddered Karin.

'She's not bad enough for that!'

'Please, Pip!' Amanda broke in quickly. 'Karin's mother becomes over-anxious when she goes near the water. Perhaps she had an accident when she was a child. Some things stay with you, fears to be conquered.'

'She drowned Francesca!' Karin shivered bleakly in the golden heat.

'I must get you into bed!' decided Amanda. 'You could be coming down with something!'

By seven o'clock that evening Karin's temperature had soared so high Doctor McGilvray had to be called. As he was delayed by a more urgent case, Rob was sent instead and Amanda showed him in to Karin's room shaken and alarmed by the high spots of fever on the tight cheekbones.

'How goes it?' Rob said cheerfully to the patient.

'I feel dreadful!' Karin croaked.

'It's not the weather for a temperature,' Rob agreed, and opened his bag. 'There's a local outbreak of rubella, you know. Has Karin come in contact with other children lately?'

'I've taken both of them, Pip and Karin, to the lion park and the bird sanctuary. There were plenty of children about, with the holidays.'

Rob bent over his patient to make his examination. 'A little congestion of the soft palate. The tonsils are slightly reddened and the eyes a little suffused.'

'I had her in the pool today. I suppose I shouldn't have, she's been listless for a day or two, but I put it down to the heat.'

'I think you'll find the spots will come out in an hour or two as the temperature goes up. It's not all that high at the moment, you know. That's a little bit of sunburn there. I've seen plenty of kids who have no fever at all. The rash usually starts at the face or neck and works downwards fairly rapidly. In most cases it fades as quickly as it develops. Pip's likely to get it too. It's highly contagious, but it has a benign course. Just keep her isolated and in bed until all the symptoms have disappeared.'

'What about complications?' Amanda asked anxiously.

'They're pretty rare.' Rob lifted his eyes from Karin to stare into Amanda's face. 'Take it easy! It's just as well she gets it now while she's a youngster. A lot of mothers I know deliberately expose their girls to German measles. Have you had it yourself?'

'I think so. I can't be sure.'

Rob smiled down at Karin, smoothing her hair away from her face. 'Well, just keep her comfortable and she'll be all right. Aspirin for the fever. Like measles, rubella is infectious for only a day or two before the eruption appears, so you'll soon know. Has she had measles?'

'Yes, I have!' Karin volunteered almost proudly.

'Then you're likely to develop rubella more easily than the child who has not. Amanda will ring me to-morrow to tell me how you're going along. Don't worry, you won't feel hot and bothered more than a day or two at the outside.' Rob put the thermometer away and snapped his bag shut. 'May I borrow Amanda for a minute or two?'

Karin didn't appear to be agreeable and Amanda said quickly, 'I'll get Brenda to stay with you until I get back.'

'All right, then,' Karin agreed with an effort. 'Don't be long!'

'I won't. That's a promise!'

Brenda was hovering in the passageway, very attached to the child despite the many one-sided battles. 'How is she?'

'German measles, Doctor Courtney thinks.'

'Doctor Courtney *knows*!' Rob corrected. 'Go in and wait with her for a few moments, would you? I'd like to speak to Amanda about her treatment.'

'Of course, Doctor!' said Brenda, smiling and visibly relieved.

'God, what a spoilt little devil!' Rob muttered sotto voce as he came down the stairs.

'She's sick and distressed, Rob!' Amanda protested a shade heatedly.

'She's all right, so don't go into a flat spin. Where are the parents, for God's sake?'

'Mr Chandler hasn't come home yet and Caroline

is keeping well away in case it's infectious. She's already torn strips off me!'

'Then why do you stay?' Rob asked with a trace of a sneer.

'Karin needs me.'

'Oh *yes*! It's very sad. A rich little girl with everything going for her and a wide circle of relatives, not to speak of a mother and father and grandmother, needs *you*!'

'For the time being!' Amanda insisted.

Mrs Harper was waiting in the entrance hall, anxious for the verdict. Amanda smiled at her and spoke almost lightly. 'Not to worry, it's German measles.'

'Thank God for that!' said Mrs Harper, glancing at the doctor. 'She's had the other kind and she was quite ill for a time. Mr Chandler rang. He wants you to ring him back, dear, after the doctor leaves. Mrs Chandler won't even talk about it. I mean, she's hardly rational about sickness!' she tacked on in a lowered, confidential tone.

'Perhaps she needs a little analysis,' Rob observed, with his dreadful memories of Caroline and his ruined Christmas Eve party.

'I'll come out to the car with you,' said Amanda with an apprehensive glance towards the top of the stairs.

'Right!' Rob took her arm and they moved out into the still hot night. 'Let's spend the weekend together?'

'What, day and night?' She saw his lips tighten.

'Why not? You know how I feel about you. And there's no need to go into shock or pull away. Sex is healthy, Amanda. Get that into your solemn little head. Living with a heavenly-minded aunt didn't do you a bit of good. You're frightened of your own body!'

'On the contrary, I just don't want to commit it to a man I'm not married to.'

'For crying out loud!' Rob cried in genuine amazement. 'You're too saintly for your own good. I've slept with plenty of girls I never married.'

'Shame!' she said dryly, not really caring who Rob slept with so long as they didn't complain.

Rob was fighting his angry frustration, pitching his bag into the back seat of his car. 'I bet you'd commit it to Chandler. He really turns you on!'

Amanda's hands clenched at her side. 'I'll ring you tomorrow Rob about Karin.'

'Karin be damned!' He jerked her to him, straining her resistant body. 'If only you'd let yourself love me. I'll even marry you, I swear it!'

'Stop it, Rob!'

She tried to bring up her hands, but he bent his head and kissed her full on the mouth, a rage of pent-up desire behind the bruising pressure. 'Mandy....' He was trembling, one hand pressing into the small of her back.

As swiftly as they had come together, they jerked apart. Headlights shone in their faces, playing over the driveway. 'Is this a set-up?' Rob asked disgustedly.

Amanda's face burned in the dark. The car swung abruptly and pulled up at the base of the steps, but it wasn't the big Mercedes but a stylish red sports car Amanda had seen before. Nonplussed, she was utterly unprepared to see Caroline, carrying a suitcase, run down the short flight of steps and on to the waiting car. 'Miss Raymond?' The voice was furious and disapproving.

'Tell her to go to hell!' Rob said tightly.

'I'd like to, but not tonight. I must go, Rob.'

'You're making that pretty clear!' he said bitterly. 'Here's to the day you come to your senses!' Without another word he got into his car and started up the engine.

'Goodnight, Rob!' she called, and walked towards Caroline's tightly controlled figure.

'If you're *quite* finished saying goodnight to your boy-friend!'

'Is there something you want?' Amanda asked with a creditable attempt at politeness.

The man in the car stared out at her, taking in her face and her slender figure and the way she pushed her hair back over her shoulder. 'Hello there, Miss Raymond.'

'Mr O'Neill,' she said coolly, feeling his sinister emanations.

'Would you mind paying attention!' Caroline said sharply. 'I'm going over to stay with my grandfather for a few days, at least until Karin is better. Brenda tells me she has German measles—is that right?'

'Yes,' Amanda answered. 'It's infectious but not at all serious.'

'I'm aware of that!' Caroline said almost passionately. 'I'm simply hopeless at nursing Karin through all her small ills. That's what *you're* paid for!'

'I'll be happy to do it for you, Mrs Chandler.'

'That's just it!' Caroline said in a shaking voice. 'You're not doing it for me at all. It's Marc you're doing it for, but you heard him, he'll never leave me.'

'I'll go inside to Karin,' said Amanda turning her head away.

'You may ring me when she recovers. I love my daughter too, Miss Raymond, though you're deliberately trying to steal her affections!'

The man Dominic coughed delicately and Caroline remembered her intention. 'What about my case, Dom? Put it in the boot.'

'Put it in yourself!' he returned steadily. 'I'm not setting foot outside this car in case Marc gets home!'

'I'll help you.' Amanda's hand tightened over the suitcase handle and Caroline allowed her to stow it in the boot of the car, standing there helpless drawing odd little sobbing breaths that sounded in the utter stillness around them.

'We'll get going,' said O'Neill, not smiling and unmoving. 'Goodnight, Miss Raymond. We'll meet again!'

Not if I can help it! Amanda thought with a shudder of repulsion. Dominic O'Neill was a handsome man, but he had a ghastly effect on her. She wanted to run.

As it was she stood there while the car pulled out of the drive with Caroline's white face averted, locked in with her difficulties and anxieties. It seemed terribly sad that such a beautiful woman should be so nerve-ridden and empty, so without sympathy for her child. *And* husband. Not that Marc Chandler appeared to be in need of it. Instinctively Amanda put thoughts about their marriage out of her mind. It was none of her business and neither of them had a thought to be free. In any case she wouldn't have the care of Karin much longer. In the first week of February the child would be returning to school and she would have no more time to undo the damage Caroline had wrought.

She drew a long breath, then went back again into

the house. She would check on Karin again, then ring Marc.

In a way Karin enjoyed the drama of her recurring little sicknesses. She lay propped up in the big bed while every member of the household came in to cluck and fuss over her. No one seemed to care in the least whether they caught Karin's dreaded rubella or not, and Pip flatly refused to be isolated, using the very good argument that the question of his future immunity had already been decided. The children had been together constantly all through the period of Karin's incubation, so there didn't seem much point in banishing Pip, and Amanda was already so fond of him she found his cheery little presence a comfort.

She had rung Marc as requested, although it had taken quite a few minutes of holding on before she was connected. As usual on the phone he sounded completely businesslike and faintly remote, raising a sharp mental picture of him at his desk, powerful, ambitious, wholly impersonal. As always too, an odd sense of shyness attacked Amanda, a persistent caution in the brain like an inbuilt warning system telling her she mustn't allow him to take hold of her mind ... her imagination. If the matter wasn't urgent he wasn't at all sure when he would be home. Amanda told him Caroline had gone to old Mr Langland and he gave an exclamation of complete exasperation as if she shouldn't bother him with such unimportant details.

She had stood beside the phone for quite a few moments after he had rung off, almost slamming down the phone in her ear. It was the woman's job to run the home, but the mistress of Four Winds seemed to run away from responsibilities without looking back. She turned away, ready to sit beside Karin's bedside all night, if need be. After all, someone had to do it, and Karin had violently repudiated Nurse Mellon's ministrations. Nurse Mellon, in fact, had packed up and left for a few days until her beloved Miss Caroline was home, or perhaps she had gone over to the Langlands. Amanda neither knew nor cared. Nurse Mellon's intense dislike of her was evident.

By the time the rest of the household was settled Karin's temperature had risen to a hundred and one and she was obviously very fretful and susceptible to a little tantrum. It appeared she couldn't bear to have Amanda out of the room, so Amanda resigned herself to a long bedside vigil in the armchair. By ten, when she went to the bed, Karin's eyes were closed and she seemed deeply asleep. Her fever was breaking because all around the hairline and the delicate little neck beads of sweat were collecting.

'Poor little girl!' Amanda whispered to the sleeping face. Very gently she turned the damp silky head, lightly sponging so as not to disturb the child, and Karin muttered but didn't open her eyes. In the faint shadow of the night lamp Amanda wasn't sure, so she drew it closer and there just behind the ears and into the scalp she saw the pink rash.

Karin muttered again and stirred restlessly so she put the lamp back on the bedside table, rearranging the sheet so that it just lightly covered Karin's lower limbs. There were no spots there, but no doubt they would cover her entire body by morning. Amanda sighed deeply and went back to her armchair. For Karin it was almost like having no mother, no blessed comfort from the woman who bore her. She couldn't understand it, and her green eyes glowed like jewels in the pale golden light. She rested her head back and tucked her bare feet beneath her, floating into a drowsy state herself. The night light made a glittering ribbon of her hair and picked up the sheen of her silk robe. There was a pain in her breast, but she had to ignore it, lest it become too urgent for her to control. After a few minutes her clenched hand fluttered down and her pale dreaming face slid further into the side of the beautiful old wing-backed chair.

'Amanda!'

She heard his voice, but she wasn't sure if she was in a dream or not.

'Wake up!'

A hand gripped her shoulder and shook it and she opened her eyes in alarm, her heart rocking, unable to grasp in her dazzled state the hard mixture of emotions in his face. Ordinarily she would have started up or at least answered him, but her heart had given a great bound so that all her breath fluttered out of her.

'It's me. I'm real enough!' His dark head was bent over her, then suddenly he swung her up into his arms while her traitorous unprotesting body curled up against him like a child. 'What did you intend doing?' he asked in an undertone, 'sitting up all night?'

She could only stare up at him, searching his brilliant eyes as though they were mirrors behind which she could read his heart and mind. Her own heart beat unmercifully, striking into his hard frame so he must feel it.

'Don't look at me like that!' he said brutally. 'I'm

going to take you to your bed and I'm going to leave you.'

The colour raced under her skin like a lick of flame. 'I believe you!' she said tautly, finding her voice.

'You *do*?' he said with bitter humour, looking down at her.

'Please put me down.'

'When I'm enjoying such innocent pleasure?' His black eyes slid over her face and her throat and the shadowed cleft of her breast. 'You're dangerous to me, Amanda!'

'Then why make it more difficult?' She shivered as if a cool stream of air was playing over her defenceless body.

'You talk too much!' Marc said abruptly, and instead of releasing her carried her through to her room, almost flinging her down on the bed so she fell in a silken huddle. Her rapid heartbeat moved the tiny bodice of her nightgown and her green eyes were huge with fright.

'Get out of that robe!' he ordered and moved to the door. 'Karin is sleeping peacefully and her fever has broken.'

The half light sheened his hair and the strong profile. He looked very dark and masculine, intolerably stimulating her senses. Her hair fell in a silver-gilt dazzle all around her face and shoulders and under no circumstances could she find her voice.

'Goodnight, little one!' he said, and it sounded both harsh and caressing. '*Don't* dream of me!'

CHAPTER EIGHT

PIP, as it happened, didn't go down with Karin's ail-
ment, but it was fully ten days before Karin felt able
to return to her lessons. She really was a delicate child,
and everyone drew a sigh of relief when it became
evident she had truly recovered and the roses had returned to her cheeks. All through her convalescence her
mother had kept away, a state of affairs that deeply
offended old Mrs Chandler, who nevertheless said not
a word, but Brenda and Mrs Harper and even that
soul of discretion, Lee, gave vent to their feelings in
the privacy of the kitchen usually over the mid-morning
cup of tea. Amanda by this time was one of them,
although she dined with the family and they all thought
of her as Karin's champion, indeed the great 'liberator',
as Mrs Harper put it.

Amanda was afterwards ashamed of herself, but on
one or two occasions she had allowed Mrs Harper the
luxury of a good gossip, and it was on these occasions
that Amanda learned many strange facts about Miss
Caroline and the late Mrs Langland. Or the facts according to Mrs Harper who worked her head off for the
master but found the mistress of the house bewildering.
Given her head Mrs Harper would have acquainted
Amanda with even more startling facts about Caroline,
but Amanda was beginning to find all the graphic word
pictures decidedly upsetting. At least she was in agreement with Mrs Harper about one thing. Caroline's

cousin Dominic O'Neill was a bad influence and he always had been—the black sheep of the Langland family, according to the garrulous but motherly Mrs Harper. Nurse Mellon was the common enemy. None of the staff liked her, even if they all agreed she was insanely protective of her Miss Caroline and she had made a good job of nursing old Mrs Chandler back to health.

Amanda, all this time, had not said a word about time off, but Marc spoke to her one morning before breakfast, calling her into his study. It was a smaller room than the library but just as distinguished, and she looked about her with interest. She had only seen into it briefly in passing, and the shutters closed against the early morning glare of the sun gave it a cool secluded appearance. Bookshelves lined the walls and there were rows of filing cabinets at one end of the room.

Marc went behind the big executive desk and picked up a few folders, stuffing them into a briefcase. With a less than happy marriage perhaps it was as well he was kept so frantically busy. His head was downbent, the winged black brows drawn together, his skin and hair so dark he looked almost foreign.

Amanda stood there while he attended very quickly to his papers, then he glanced up at her, a bitter-sweet half smile on his handsome mouth. 'Don't think because I've been busy I haven't known how marvellously you've been coping. Mamma sings your praises the moment I lay eyes on her!'

'It's nice of you to say so.'

'Don't be cutting, little one. It doesn't suit you.'

'Surely you'll permit me a comment?' The colour of her coral printed dress added impact to her eyes and the light gold of her summer tan, so that she looked slightly different, more daring and undeniably softly-sexy.

'You'll be permitted more than that!' he said smoothly, coming round the desk with such dynamic intent that she fell back a pace.

He laughed, his black eyes sardonic, so she felt foolish and shaken. 'It's all right . . . all right. . . .' He looked at her, his voice slowed to a drawl. 'I was only going to suggest a break for you. God knows you're entitled to it.'

'And where would I go?' Amanda looked up at him, her green eyes very clear and direct.

'Anywhere you like. Say the word, I'll arrange it. We have a beach house on the Coast. You could fly there for a few days. Or you might prefer the city lights.'

She seemed almost flustered, her eyes deepening with colour. 'If I went to the beach I don't suppose I could take the children.'

'Why on earth would you want to?'

'Because I care about them and I enjoy their company. We could have fun and it would do Karin good.'

Marc regarded her intently. 'I'll have to think about it.'

'Don't you trust me?'

'I don't want you and the children on your own. I trust you, of course, but you'll need some kind of protection.'

'Isn't there a telephone? What are you expecting?'

He looked down at her coolly. 'My dear child, you'll turn enough heads without drawing them to your door, and you couldn't possibly be the mother of two children.'

'I never thought of that!' she sighed, and her head tipped over like a flower on a stalk.

'Lee can go with you. There are separate quarters to the rear of the house and he'll be on hand if he's needed. He's small, but he's exquisitely capable of dispatching even the most ferocious assailant—one of the talents I dare say you're not aware of. I met Lee in a back street of Hong Kong years ago. Some psycopath was trying to pull a knife on me at the time. Lee had him bent backwards before I even had time to turn around.'

'Would he want to go?' Amanda asked.

'He'll do anything to please me and the change will do him good. Leave it with me. I'll get everything arranged today. There's no use suggesting my mother should join you—she has a thing about flying and I want her right where I can see her at the moment. She's doing beautifully, but she's not completely well.'

'And Mrs Chandler?' she asked.

'Don't be a damned fool!' he said softly.

'But she might object?' Amanda couldn't help herself.

'Leave me to handle the dramatics. Caroline forgets her daughter for long stretches—or haven't you noticed?' Amanda didn't answer and he moved abruptly away from her and to the door. 'Have you everything you need?'

'You pay me more than enough!'

'Then you've no idea of your true value. So long, little one. I'll try to get away early tonight. Karin's looking at me as if I'm a stranger.'

'No, she loves you!' Amanda corrected. 'She just misses you, that's all.'

'In that case we'd better have a family dinner. Tell Mrs Harper, will you? She needs little encouragement to turn on a banquet and the children will enjoy it.'

Amanda smiled and Marc returned her smile, but she knew he had nothing to give her but heartache and pain. It was a very sad and lonely thing to love where there was no hope. 'Shall I tell the children about the holiday or will you?'

'I'll just have time to tell Caroline, and I'd better do it now!'

For the next ten minutes until he had left the house, Amanda held her breath. For some peculiar, unexplained reason she had the feeling that this time Caroline was going to object violently, if only because of her cold disapproval of Amanda. The day passed and Caroline said nothing, seemingly indifferent to the proposed holiday. After lunch she went out, not saying where, and when she turned back to catch Amanda and Brenda staring after her, her pale blue eyes shone with a hard light.

'I can't say I particularly enjoy family dinners, but I'll be home this evening. My husband wants me!'

Her tall figure against the background of sun and trees looked thin to the point of emaciation, but her clothes as usual were exquisite, chosen with much taste and style. She walked out on to the colonnaded porch, then down to her waiting car, and Brenda turned back to her dusting, muttering silently.

'At least she doesn't seem to mind about the holiday!' Amanda said out aloud, caught up in the pulsing tension Caroline created at will.

'Why should she?' Brenda sniffed. 'It's him she wants —Mr Marc. It's not proper the way she feels for him, not caring how she hurts him or the child and never letting go.'

'Well, they only have to answer to each other, Brenda!'

'And the child!' Brenda replied emphatically. 'You're a nice girl and you're too kind. I've been in this house for eight years and I've seen a lot. Why he hasn't left her I'll never know, in spite of her beauty. She's a feverish kind of a woman, never happy yet she's got everything in this world!'

Just at that moment Nurse Mellon came down the stairs, her face rigid and sightless. It was obvious she had overheard Brenda, but Brenda didn't even blush. Karin appeared behind her in her pretty yellow dress, then Pip and Amanda murmured a polite greeting to the nurse and called to the children. In spite of the restraining presence of the nurse they raced down the stairs and she caught at their hands to take them out into the garden. The sky was blue and radiant, but there were clouds building up on the horizon. A thunderstorm had been forecast, but while they almost nightly blew up into spectacular displays no real rain had fallen yet. But it was coming, and this sun-hot tropical paradise would steam with thundering torrents. While it was exciting it was no joke, and Amanda decided she had best get the extra clothes she needed for the holiday from the house. It wouldn't take her long and Brenda could look after the children for the space of an hour or so.

Insects were fluttering inside the house when she let

herself in and she wondered how they had got there. She stared around her at her old home, dully illuminated because of the closed shutters and the darkening sky outside. Tenderly she imagined her aunt coming out to greet her, but she was alone in the house. She moved through every room, slightly alarmed by the moths that fluttered past her. Why, they could eat all the rugs! She bent down to inspect the precious old Persian rug in the living room, but miraculously it seemed intact. Before she did anything else she would have to clear the house of the gauzy invaders. There was dusting to be done as well, for despite the closed windows and shutters a film of dust lay over all the polished surfaces, the sight of which would have thrown her aunt into a state of ecstatic horror.

She turned on a few lights in the gloomy house and opened the front and back doors. There was no sign of Mrs Farrell, her nearest neighbour. Indeed the house looked shut up, and then Amanda remembered she often went on visits to each of her three married daughters, all of whom now lived in Brisbane. A pity! She would have liked to have spoken to Mrs Farrell, although she had rung her at Christmas. The house seemed oppressively still, almost haunted, neglected, and it was affecting her mood.

'For heaven's sake get a grip on yourself!' she said out loud, and snatched up a duster. Some of the moths had already flown out of the doors and she would dispatch the rest of them with a spray. As she worked all her childhood memories seemed to come back to her and often her eyes burned with a green fire. By the time the furniture was gleaming again she felt a little cheered. The dining room suite was actually magnificent in a dark, Victorian kind of way. Aunt Claire had always thrown a fit whenever the cat jumped up on to the table, threatening to smash the ruby glass épergne. Her aunt's presence she felt so closely it was almost like having a gentle ghost behind her.

Afterwards she washed up in the bathroom before searching out her beach clothes. There was a big dark green straw hat, a tourist kind of thing, that would protect her skin. The thing was to find it. Her shorts and brief tops she had never worn at the Chandlers', but they would be ideal for the beach.

In her preoccupation she started violently when the front door banged shut. She jumped off the chair she was standing on so she could search the top of the wardrobe and ran almost frightened to the front of the house, throwing open the door. No human being greeted her, but a livid sky. She looked up at it with eyes wide. A peculiar fragrance like incense hung in the air. There was no wild gust of wind now, but the parrots were screeching loudly in the umbrella trees. She had delayed too long and the storm seemed imminent. There was something unreal about the sky, something intolerable about the livid green through the dark grape of the storm clouds. The clouds were lowering, stooping over her, menacing. Her young face went pale and she told herself very slowly that she had to fight out of her own particular fear of electrical storms. For years she had done it and she had the house for protection. She had no intention of driving out in the car until it was over. Probably like all tropical storms it would be volcanic but brief.

Quite a big lizard ran out of the floorboards and over her foot and she gave a little nervous shriek. This was ridiculous! She took a deep breath, put the stopper against the front door and went inside to finish her packing. Mentally she had to prepare herself for the dangerous phenomenon of forked lightning. Lightning that could split asunder a giant tree like so much match-wood trapping ... trapping ... her hands were trembling and she shook her head dazedly as if to clear it. She was doing this to herself and she had to stop. Why didn't the shrieking parrots go away, fly to safety?

She located the straw hat from Fiji and threw it down on the bed. Through the bedroom window she could see the pearly black storm clouds hovering just above the magnificent old mango tree she had played in as a child. Why didn't it just rain? The waiting was the worst part. In another minute the house lights dulled and a quite terrifying burst of thunder shook the timber supports of the old house. Amanda felt her stomach muscles knotting and caught sight of her paper white face in the mirror. Her eyes looked a little strange, brilliant but filled with the silly terror she didn't seem able to control. She had endured years of thunderstorms before now, but at least she hadn't had to bear them alone.

She sat down on the side of the bed and put her head down. The storm would spend itself and then she would drive back to the house. Probably old Mrs Chandler would be anxious; she had told Amanda to be back before the storm. Thunder rolled and cracked again like a massive bombardment, then the rain turned on with its amazing suddeness, assaulting the iron roof. Perhaps there would be hail, great chunks of it, like the time all the windows on one side of the house had been broken. The roof was so old, dating back to her grandfather's time. Would it hold?

What happened next was quite alarming until Amanda realised someone was hammering on the door. She felt faint for a minute, disbelieving, and her legs would scarcely support her.

'Amanda?'

Her nerves jumped in shock. She would know that voice anywhere. Unconsciously she tried to square her shoulders, drawing herself up and moving to the bedroom door.

'Marc!'

He looked a little pale under his dark tan, his black eyes sparkling like jets, his hair and his polished skin sheened with rain. 'Why the devil don't you answer your phone?' he demanded with harsh arrogance.

'It didn't ring!' she said jerkily, hoping he wouldn't notice the ridiculous tremble in her body.

He threw his damp jacket down on a chair. The cream and tan striped shirt beneath was dry and he loosened his tie and turned up the cuffs of his shirt. 'My dear child, no lines are out yet so far as I know. Where is it?'

'Just behind you.'

She gestured to the little alcove, looking very pale and fragile, watching him pick up the receiver and exclaim impatiently: 'It's not even on the hook!'

She shut her eyes, swaying a little. 'I was trying to tidy up. I suppose I knocked it.'

'Are you all right?'

Her eyes flew open again and she found him watching her intently, his face strangely taut, his temper finely balanced. 'I was worried!'

'Did you come for me?' she asked gently. 'I have the car.'

'I *know* that!' His head was thrown back, the black hair closely curling in the rain, and he looked as handsome and arrogant as the devil. 'This is a lonely kind of place, almost melancholy, and you're on your own. Whatever did you come for anyway?'

'Just to get a few things!' She was stammering slightly and he came nearer her, dropping a hard hand on her shoulder.

'Do storms frighten you?'

'A little.'

'A damned lot, I'd say!'

He looked so extraordinarily dominant and vital she made a strange little sound. 'Well? Everyone is frightened of something, aren't they? Except you.'

'I'll take you back,' he said flatly. 'The car will be all right here.'

'No, Marc. I'm not going!'

There was a touch of hysteria in the jewelled flash of her eyes. 'Who are you to call me Marc?' he asked tersely, his eyes roving over her with something like hostility.

'But I have, haven't I?' She gave a funny little laugh and leaned back against the wall as if for support.

The house lights were dipping and waning and the rain on the roof was a continuous roar, blocking out rational thoughts.

His glance sharpened and there was a biting inflection in his voice. 'We can't stay here, Amanda. That would be even more insane than driving out in a thunderstorm. Come with me, little one. I won't let anything hurt you.'

She tried to take hold of herself, coming away from the wall and lifting her head. 'It's a silly thing, I know!'

'Your whole body is shaking!'

She flung him a shimmering green glance, a little colour seeping in to her cheekbones. 'I'll get my raincoat. But what about you? An umbrella would be useless.'

'To hell with that!' he said with crisp decision. 'Let's get going!' He looked very vital and taunting, totally male. Too contemptuous even to make fun of her. Amanda moved along the hallway looking very young and desperate, and just then a clap of thunder broke over them like the end of the world.

She gave a stifled little moan and fell back against the wall, putting her shaking hands to her temples. 'I don't want to, Marc. I *can't*!'

'Stop it! *Immediately!*' He was beside her, pulling her violently into his arms.

'Just hold me!' She brushed her gleaming blonde head back and forth against his chest. 'Hold me. I no longer remember who you are, what you are!'

He seemed to answer with a great effort, his dark face betraying that for once his emotions weren't under their habitual tight control. 'Amanda, do you have any idea what could happen?'

'No.' She lay for a moment against his breast, a tired child, no seductress. All her vitality seemed consumed, her nerves shaken. He was the only strength in the world and she could hear the heavy thud of his heart.

'It *can't be*!' With one hand he grasped her long hair and pulled it back like a punishment, straining her face to him.

'But I want *nothing*!' she protested despairingly, her eyes filled with tears, enormous and darkly green.

'God help me, but *I* do!' he muttered harshly.

She heard the furious intake of breath as if he meant to teach her a lesson, then his mouth was on hers, provoking an instant of extreme agitation like a seizure. A confusion of emotions raged in her breast and some of the wild freedom of the storm. She opened her soft, sweet mouth to him and he claimed it with urgency, his hands sliding up the small of her back, holding her body in to him so that the tiny buttons on his shirt bit into her skin.

'Why didn't you run from me?' he muttered against the heated satin of her skin.

Amanda couldn't answer even if she wanted to, because his mouth covered hers again, exploring it deeply, calling up convulsive spurts of excitement. She felt weak and dizzy with longing, her eyes closed, her heavy lashes dewed with tears. If this was to be her one small share of happiness in all the world then it was worth the inevitable pain. She wasn't even afraid of him, though she knew she couldn't stop him, his lovemaking dangerous, elemental, even tragic, brought on by the fury of the storm.

He held her hard, moving his mouth down the soft cream of her throat, murmuring her name, demanding she arch her body so that it perfectly fitted his own. His beautiful long-fingered hands moved over her sloping shoulders, encountered the tiny ruched bodice of her sun-dress and pushed it relentlessly aside.

She gave a little gasp of shock he took no account of, driven by the imperious male need to know the body of the female. She had never experienced such intimacy and she was moaning wordlessly while his hands closed over her breasts, taking the tender weight of them, the dusky tips going taut with yearning. The excitement was shattering. She didn't think she could bear it. Now that his hands claimed the smooth contours of her body she was overcome by a terrible, piercing desire, an inability to withstand him.

Outside there was a great flash of sheet lightning, the rain blown about on a high wind. She no longer noticed it, nor the tumultuous crash of thunder. She was out of control, existing for only one thing—to give pleasure to this one man. Marc lifted her high in his arms, his eyes never leaving her. Her shining hair streamed over his arm and the flame of wonder was there in her face and the pulsing of her soft lovely mouth.

'*Love me!*' she murmured, her eyes tightly closed.

'Now?' he asked tautly, 'will I make you mine completely?'

'Yes!'

A vein pulsated in his temple and for a moment his dark face was touched with a pagan ruthlessness. 'I wanted to long ago!'

She felt the tremble in his strong arms then he carried her through to the bedroom as if nothing mattered except that he have his way. She murmured his name and he turned her out of his arms so that she fell on to the bed, her hair streaming out and caught under her.

'Almost I could do it,' he muttered with harsh gravity, 'but I care too damned much!'

'You don't care at all!' she cried in a strange state of shock and separation.

'Do you want me to be the first man?'

'I love you!' she whispered, softly stricken. 'I only want what you want!'

Very gently he bent over and covered her breasts. 'I can't betray you, Amanda, even when I so badly want to!'

'Forgive me, I don't want to make anything hard for you!' She twisted her silver-gilt head to one side.

'I should never have touched you,' he said austerely. 'I told myself I never would again, but somehow you drove everything else from my mind. You'll forget me and I'm going to give you that chance.'

'I'll never forget you until I die!' The tears streaked down her face and she turned her head into the quilted pillow.

The hand that stroked her hair now was the same hand that smoothed Karin's soft, silky curls. 'There'll be someone else for you,' he said deliberately. 'Someone with his whole life to offer you. Not Courtney, he's not half good enough, but some fine young man with ambition and integrity.'

'I don't want anyone else but you!'

'Don't cry, Amanda!' he begged.

'I can't help it. When do I have to go, *tell* me?'

'Do you think I like my life?' he asked tensely, responding to her broken tone.

'Oh, leave me, I'll get over it!' She put both hands to her aching head. 'I knew the consequences would be tragic. I suppose I was born to love you and suffer for it.'

'You'll have to go away!' he said harshly. 'If you stay I'll surely take you.'

Her green eyes flew open and he looked at her, then

bent and slowly kissed her mouth. 'I must arrange it that you're safe. I have duties, responsibilities, Amanda, and I can't forsake them. Not even for you.'

She shivered and lay quietly under his hand. 'I think I must be very unlucky. I seem to lose all the people I love!'

Marc shook his dark head. 'There'll be happiness for you, Amanda. Believe in yourself. Believe you'll find it. You have everything to offer a man. Everything that's precious!'

She tried to smile at him, forcing her trembling lips to curve. 'I love you, Marc Chandler. I always will!'

He put the tips of his fingers across her mouth, stemming the flow of words. 'In another year you won't remember me, and I'll be glad!'

Swiftly he moved to the door, turning his dark head towards the lightening sky. 'The storm is almost over,' he said with something like bitterness. 'I'll wait for you in the car.'

He left her, and Amanda knew with a crushing finality that he wasn't going to allow her to undermine his plans for her future. She would have to go away and she would have to accept his help. But she would never forget the man she was forbidden to love.

Marc scarcely spoke a word to her at dinner that night, but it didn't seem to matter. Caroline had made one of her extraordinary transitions from feverish, blazing rage to an amiable languor. She sat at the table toying with food and wine, and now and again her narrow exquisite lips turned up like a feline with a delicious treat in store. Her voice when she spoke Amanda's name should have made her wary, but it didn't. She was too caught up in her despairing thoughts and even the children found their consistently sunny-natured Mandy withdrawn and quiet. Bedtime came as a relief, although the children were restless for more of Marc's company, but he never came along the east wing to their rooms, kissing them goodnight from the foot of the stairs.

Amanda slept badly, expecting tomorrow would only bring Marc's decision. Old Mrs Chandler went out next morning, driven over to her sister-in-law's place by Lee, and Brenda and Mrs Harper took the opportunity to slip into town. It was such a hot day Amanda proposed little more than a few lessons on the lawn and perhaps a trip to the lake with its cool green surroundings. Caroline too had gone out, very early for her and the big house seemed to hold a certain menace for all its Colonial splendour. Nurse Mellon's company was something to be avoided and she had been giving Amanda piercing glances all morning.

They were almost ready to leave for the lake when Caroline returned to the house, finding her way along to Amanda's room where the children were waiting for Amanda to put a few of her things in the big yellow beach bag. Their little faces were subdued, sensing Amanda's saddened preoccupation, but they looked positively fearful when Caroline swept through the door communicating a tremendous purpose.

'Leave that, Miss Raymond!' she said sharply, reaching for Karin's hand and jerking the child to her side. 'I have other plans for my daughter!' Her voice was slurred with excitement and her light eyes sparkled menacingly, the pupil, a mere pinpoint in the palely illuminated iris.

Pip stood close to Amanda now as if to protect her

and Amanda felt him slip his hand into her own. Her own she tightened gently, fixing Caroline with a clear, straight look. 'Are you taking her out for the day, Mrs Chandler?'

'That's my business!' Caroline's chiselled face contorted in a fury.

'I don't want to go!' Karin wailed.

'Shut up!' her mother snapped as if all patience was failing her. 'I'd better explain, Miss Raymond. I have no intention of allowing you to take my daughter anywhere. In fact, I have important news for you. I'm taking her myself!'

'Where, Mrs Chandler?' Amanda asked calmly as if she was really interested.

'Why, I'm not sure!' Caroline faltered. 'I'm not like you, Miss Raymond. I don't think clearly all the time, but I'm able to take my daughter where and whenever I like!'

'Is it for the day, Mrs Chandler?' Amanda persisted, alarmed by Caroline's unnatural manner.

'Are you *mad*?' Caroline shouted. 'I'm taking her on a trip.'

For a minute Amanda's heart nearly failed her. Caroline's alabaster skin was beaded with perspiration and the long-fingered white hands were twitching, twitching.... She looked driven, almost unbalanced, and Karin seemed too frightened to run to Amanda in spite of the appeal that rayed out of her eyes.

Instinct told Amanda not to cross her, but somehow she had to get to the phone. Marc had told her repeatedly that Karin was to go nowhere alone with her mother. 'I suppose you'll want clothes packed, then,

Mrs Chandler?' she asked easily, pressing a warning into Pip's hand.

Caroline broke into a stammering laugh. 'I expected you to fight me, Miss Raymond!'

'Why on earth should I do that? You're Karin's mother. Shall I pack a suitcase for you?'

A stifled sob broke from Karin and Caroline's expression betrayed her astonishment. 'I was going to buy everything new,' she said in a bewildered mutter.

'Why bother?' Amanda said pleasantly. 'Karin has so many lovely clothes and it shouldn't take me long to get them together. I'll just have to run downstairs for a moment. Brenda's pressed quite a few of Karin's dresses, but she hasn't brought them upstairs as yet.' Amanda could hardly endure to look at Karin's anguished little face. 'I won't be a moment.'

'Come here!' Caroline ordered in a dangerous voice, and Amanda turned back with her heart in her mouth, but Caroline was only telling the cowering children to sit down and wait.

She flew down the stairs and on to the library, desperate now to get through to Marc. It could take ages, and she had the strange feeling she would never talk to him again. The finger that dialled the mine's number was trembling so much she had to start again, cursing herself under her breath. The children were suffering and her whole being was concentrated on getting Marc home to take charge of the situation. Caroline in her present mood was utterly beyond her. Those hands twitching constantly, those glittering eyes. Was she unbalanced or drugged or what?

The phone rang twice at the other end before a thin, cruel hand covered her own and twisted her arm behind her. 'Naughty, naughty!' Dominic O'Neill whispered against her ear. 'Don't tell me you were ringing Marc? We can't allow that!'

His face was very close to hers and she could feel the curious excitement in him. *'Let me go!'* She was breathing quickly and her green eyes were frantic with disgust.

'Hush!' he whispered again. 'I don't want to hurt you. At least not like this!'

Her arm and shoulder were aching unbearably and he pushed her before him, making mocking noises. 'Does Marc already have you for a lover?'

'No answer? I suppose he'd marry you if he could, but he's already trapped into holy wedlock—and she *did* trap him, you know. Lovely, mad Caro!'

Her voice was tremulous with a mixture of fright and anger. 'If you can call her that, how can you let her take Karin? Children must be protected.'

'Must they?' he murmured in an idle voice. 'I never thought about it before. Up the stairs, Goldilocks. You realise, of course, Caro will be very angry with you.'

'That's nothing to what will happen to you!' Amanda retorted boldly. 'Karin is very important to her father, and it seems to me you're participating in a kidnap!'

He wrenched her against him and she recoiled from the touch of his body. 'Don't talk like a fool. Possession is nine tenths of the law, and Caro *is* the mother. Besides, I'd do anything to score off Marc. Handsome, brilliant, tough and determined Marc Chandler. I feel as strongly about him as you do, dear girl, but for different reasons. My grandfather thinks a thousand times more of Marc than he ever will of me. Even my dear parents follow suit. *My friends*. Marc set the pattern for my life. Compared to him I'm a waster, and everyone did compare us, you know. We were great friends as boys.'

'You're hurting me!' Amanda said in a cool, contemptuous voice.

'And enjoying it. Until this moment I didn't realise how much!'

The pain was making her hazy and even if he broke her arm she wasn't going to appeal to him again. At the door of her bedroom he let go of her and pushed her before him into the room. 'This treacherous little bitch was trying to ring Marc!'

'You . . .!' Caroline snapped accusingly, and advanced across the room like a tigress, slapping Amanda across the side of the face. 'How dare you try to trick me!'

'Mr O'Neill was mistaken!' Amanda said with cold loathing. 'I was trying to contact Mrs Chandler. I'm supposed to drive her back home.'

'You're lying!'

'She is *not*!' Pip stoutly declared. 'I heard Gran tell her myself.'

'Then she can wait!' Caroline said suddenly, a tiny pulse beating at the base of her throat. 'Sometimes you make me sick, Dom!'

The sudden division between them gave Amanda confidence. 'Can't the children wait in the schoolroom until you're ready, Mrs Chandler?'

Caroline stared at her as though trying to ponder what went on in Amanda's mind. 'I don't care where they wait just so long as you hurry up.'

'Don't think up any more tricks!' Dominic O'Neill came back to Amanda and grasped her arm painfully.

'I'm awake to you if poor little Caro isn't!'

'My only concern is for the children,' Amanda said truthfully. 'They should be sitting quietly.'

'Get on with it!' Caroline suddenly yelled. 'We have an agreement!'

'Yes, Mrs Chandler.' Amanda submissively bowed her blonde head and shepherded the frightened children into the schoolroom, with Dominic O'Neill hovering in the hallway ready to pounce like a hawk.

Before she touched the doorknob Amanda knew what she was going to do. 'Trust me!' she called to the children, and thrust them through the doorway, slamming the heavy panelled door shut and swiftly turning the key. Her heart seemed to be exploding in her throat and she raced towards the sitting room with O'Neill close behind her, flinging the key in a glittering arc through the wide open window so it fell far below to the rose garden.

'You bitch!' The man struck her hard, a greenish pallor under his skin.

Caught off balance, she went down under the blow, further striking her head against the antique oval table in the centre of the room.

Caroline, breathing deeply, ran to the door staring at them with wild, glittering eyes. 'What's happened?'

'She's thrown the key through the window, that's what's happened!' her cousin snarled at her. 'Why don't you carry off your kid by yourself?'

'You promised you'd help me,' Caroline said slowly, in what seemed to Amanda as shocked surprise. 'Didn't you promise to help me, Dom?'

'Ah, for God's sake!' He approached Amanda as if he was going to hit her again and Amanda's whole body grew rigid as she anticipated the blow.

'Go and get the key, Dom!' Caroline begged with fresh anxiety. 'Someone could come home.'

'Just so long as it's not Marc, I don't give a damn!' He looked down at Amanda, but she refused to look back at his narrow, sinister face. 'I'm going to get even with you, girlie!'

'Leave her alone!' Caroline said suddenly. 'She has courage—I have to give her that much. Get the key, Dom. It couldn't have gone far.'

'Surely you don't think I'm going to grovel on my hands and knees?' he demanded in outrage.

'Why not? It would suit you!' Amanda blazed abruptly.

'I liked you, I really did!' he said oddly, his lean figure clearly silhouetted against the brilliant sunlight.

'Don't move or I'll kill you!' a voice said from the doorway, sounding so incredibly menacing Caroline swung about screaming:

'Marc!'

'You dare to come into my house. You dare to remove my child. And what were you going to do to Amanda?' The brilliant black eyes regarded the silent man sombrely.

'Nothing, I swear!' Dominic O'Neill seemed to brace himself.

'No?' Marc moved so fast none of them saw the blow that dropped O'Neill like a puppet, sending him sprawling across the vibrantly coloured rug. He reached downwards again and jerked the supine figure to its feet, looking as if he was about to repeat the blow.

'Please, Marc, the children are in the schoolroom. I locked them in!' Amanda tried to struggle to her feet, but her appeal came too late to help O'Neill.

Marc hit him again, seeming to take a remote pleasure in the sharp crack of the blow. He was taller and
more powerfully built than his adversary and this time
O'Neill went reeling into the wall, crashing his
shoulder.

'Get out!' Marc said dully. Get out while you can!'

O'Neill's face gleamed bone white. 'Why don't you
finish it? You could smash me to pulp!'

'You're a fool, Dom!' Marc said in a low, hard tone.
'You've let Caro twist you around her little finger so
often, so long, I don't know which one of you is guilty
of the greater corruption.'

Caroline's voice broke in a sob, and she covered her
contorted face with her hands. 'Dom's the only one
who's ever been kind to me in my life.'

'Kind? Oh no!' Dominic O'Neill said jaggedly. 'I
could have helped you plenty of times, but I didn't.'

'Leave her!' Marc ordered. 'You've done too much
harm already. If she's nearly broken you have to take
a lot of the blame.'

'Blame the family!' O'Neill said with a faintly hys-
terical laugh. 'You didn't know, did you, Marc, and
they were all such aristocrats, they didn't tell you!'

Marc had moved towards Amanda, lifting her to her
feet. 'You don't deserve any of this!'

'She rang you, didn't she?' Caroline flared back
abruptly.

'On the contrary, I did, Miss Caroline!' Nurse Mellon stood near the door pressing a handkerchief to her
lips. 'Come with me, my dear. You're not well.'

Caroline stared with her light blue eyes. 'You rang
Marc?'

'It was necessary!' Nurse Mellon said in a voice Amanda had never heard before; soft and shaken. 'I see now how wrong I've been. I do hope you'll forgive me, Mr Chandler. You too, Miss Raymond. You have always acted in the best interests of the child.'

'Forgive me if I have to tear myself away!' Dominic O'Neill said jeeringly.

'Yes, yes, go!' Caroline cried hysterically. 'You've always been afraid of Marc.'

'Come with me, Miss Caroline. Come to your room.' Nurse Mellon stood by helplessly, looking as if she was about to weep.

Caroline turned on her calling her a name Amanda wished she had never heard, but this, instead of profoundly shocking the nurse, seemed to bring her right out of her shamed distress. 'That will do!' she said curtly. 'You are certainly not well.'

Dominic O'Neill lifted his hand in a parody of a salute and started on his way out of the house, a state of affairs that started Caroline off in a fresh rage.

She looked about her wildly, then her eyes fell on the scrap of embroidery Amanda had started Karin on as an interest. Sharp scissors lay beside the open sewing box and Caroline snatched them up, lurching at Amanda, caught up in a dreadful annihilating passion.

'*You* did this to me!'

Even above Nurse Mellon's incoherent cry Amanda was conscious of the mindless blaze in Caroline's eyes. They were too bright, straining, and the round spots of colour were unnaturally harsh on her cheekbones, playing up the pronounced pallor.

Amanda closed her eyes as the room tilted drunkenly.

The blow to her temple had dazed her and in an instant
the twin blades of the scissors would strike her. Where,
her unprotected face or her body? Either way the
effect would be ruinous.

From long experience Marc moved with speed and
strength, deflecting the blow and grasping at his wife's
wrist, but she struggled like a madwoman using her
brief spasm of super-strength to gash the arm that held
her. Blood spurted instantly all along the wound and
Caroline gave a shrill cry and dropped the scissors she
had used as a weapon.

'Marc!' Her voice sounded tortured.

'Take her to her room. Blood always worries her,'
he said to the nurse almost normally.

'But, Mr Chandler?' Nurse Mellon looked appalled
at his torn and bloodied shirt sleeve.

'Please do as I ask!' he said tersely. 'I think you'll
find my wife is on the point of collapse. Amanda can
ring Doctor McGilvray. He knows the problem.'

Nurse Mellon led the quietly sobbing Caroline away,
almost voiceless with shock. She was worse in her way
than her charge, because she had blindly shut her eyes
to all the signs. So many times she had been persuaded
by Caroline's fluttering insistence, but at least her
hideous uneasiness had driven her into ringing the
child's father. Nurse Mellon left the room with an
acrid taste in her mouth, while Caroline went meekly
as though all thoughts of violence had ebbed away from
her.

Amanda looked sickly at Marc's injured arm. He
was holding it under the elbow, but there was no
change in him except for a certain carven indifference.

'I'll have to let the children out, then I'll ring the doctor.'

'Lee's already taken them out of the house. There are duplicate keys for every room in the house,' he replied.

'I didn't know. Neither, thank God, did Mrs Chandler.'

'Why should she?' he said briefly. 'She's never taken the slightest interest in the running of the house. Lee knows where they're kept, and I won't forget him for his quick-wittedness and his devotion to this family. At least that fool woman came to her senses. Caroline has been addicted to barbiturates for years. Since she was a schoolgirl she was swallowing tablets to help her through her day. Dom and his circle were a sinister influence, but at the time I married her her fluctuating moods seemed no more than a highly strung temperament spoiled rotten. She was very beautiful and she could be very gay and charming, but I married her for the wrong reason. I didn't love her, but in those days I wasn't in the pursuit of love. I was too damned ambitious, too damned certain of where I was going to go. Our families were very close and it was always expected we would marry, so I entered into the perfect marriage of convenience. The consequences you can see.

'Caroline is utterly dependent on me no matter how she behaves and it's my duty to closely watch her until the day she dies. Her family knew of her addiction, of course, but they didn't think to tell me. Later old Douglas told me they prayed our marriage would give Caroline the stability she needed, but she's suffered a mental and physical deterioration since Karin's birth. She screamed for days when she knew she was pregnant and I've taken good care she never fell pregnant again. That was one source of her terrors, and she has no defences against stress or strain. If our marriage has failed I'm going to take the blame. Caroline was and always will be an irresponsible child, but she pays for it. She suffers in her own way while she's giving the rest of us hell. I've wanted my mother away from the house many times, but she refuses to leave. She loves me and she loves Karin, and mostly between us we keep the situation under control.'

Amanda shook her blonde head, her young face soft with compassion. 'You didn't have to tell me, Marc.'

'I want you to understand,' he said, and his face grew taut. 'I have to send you away, Amanda, for your own safety. It will break Karin's heart, but now it's an absolute necessity.'

'I understand,' she said gallantly. 'I'll go and ring Doctor McGilvary now. That arm needs attention.'

She went to the door and stopped there, a slender girl who in the space of a few short months had turned into a woman. 'Things will come right for you, Marc, you'll see, and I'll pray every day of my life for Karin.'

'You *must*!' he said, and his brilliant black eyes flashed. 'I want to settle money on you, Amanda. You've helped Karin more than anyone else in her life.'

'No, Marc!' she shook her head dully. 'I don't want it. I won't starve, you know. I can always get a job.'

'You'll have it all the same!' he said vehemently, and for the first time there was a pallor under the teak tan of his skin. 'It's all I can give you, and you must have it. You're aware I care for you.'

'Yes,' she said abruptly, and ran away before he could see the tears in her eyes.

CHAPTER NINE

WINTER in the city was cold, but at least it was far away from the heat and spice of the tropics and there was little to remind Amanda of the world she had left. The first six months had been dreadful, almost a battle to get through the day with the worst to come through the long, lonely nights. Marc so filled her mind, he seemed more vivid, more compelling locked up in her memory than ever before, and as a result she never really succeeded at anything she tried to do.

The city was like a jungle full of noise and madly rushing people and automobiles that bore down on her every time she tried to cross the streets, and her eyes followed every tall, dark-haired, dark-eyed strange man who just happened to bear a superficial resemblance to Marc. For the six months she suffered badly, then she began to pull herself together. She had no right to turn her back on the world, when there were so many with so much more to bear. Despite her distressed protests, Marc had settled enough money on her to keep her in utter idleness, but with customary obstinacy she had refused to use it except to find herself a suitable place to live. Besides, work was her salvation and she accepted the first job the secretarial agency sent her to: an accountant's office in the main street of the city. She spent only three months there, then she found herself a much better job as assistant to the secretary of one of the country's top fashion designers, an attractive, very gifted woman called Martina Linden.

After that of necessity, Amanda's social contacts began to multiply, then when Martina suggested she model some of her exclusive label for certain customers and buyers she found she had to pay a great deal of attention to her appearance. Her blonde beauty and the faint air of mystery about her had already drawn a flood of admirers, but no one apart from Marc Chandler was ever to move her heart.

Once in the office with Martina sitting opposite her busily sketching away and using Amanda's face and slender body as an inspiration, she had fainted dead away. Martina had jumped up exclaiming and calling, but Amanda had only been out for a few seconds. If anyone had bothered to snatch up the papers she had been reading they would perhaps have noticed a small column given over to reporting the death of Mrs Caroline Louise Chandler, wife of mining magnate Mr Marc Chandler of Mount Regina Mine, who had been tragically killed in a car accident. The Coroner had brought in a verdict of death by misadventure because the car Mrs Chandler had been driving had failed to take a bend in the road and gone into the river. Death had been by drowning.

Martina had immediately sent out for food, thinking Amanda was starving herself, and now that she thought about it working far too hard, but Amanda had been shaking so much Martina had finally sent her home to her own sister for a few days, realising something was very wrong but not knowing what. Sophy was such a splendid, good-natured woman with such a capacity for listening she would get the full story out of the child, but Amanda, though she came to like and trust

Sophy, never told anyone. She spent only three days with Sophy, then she returned to work, while Martina continued to have extra food sent in in case Amanda really wasn't looking after herself.

The weeks passed, then the months, but Amanda heard nothing from any member of the Chandler family, not that they would know where she was living. Marc had wanted her completely out of his life, so future contact with the family had been impossible despite the dreadful day when she had to say her good-byes and their affection for her had been touchingly revealed. Karin had hidden, refusing to come down, but Pip had stood with his grandmother, both pairs of brown eyes shining with tears. Marc's mother had given her a very beautiful antique necklace 'in gratitude' and Amanda treasured it though she had never worn it, leaving it until such time as she was indifferent to her pain of loss.

It was hopeless to cling to her memories. Tormented, unhappy Caroline was gone and Marc would have little difficulty in finding some other woman to mother his child any moment he cared to lift a finger. He hadn't written a word or contacted her in any way, so she was forced to conclude that what little feeling he had had for her was now gone. She understood. She was part of his unhappy past and now she too was over the shock of Caroline's death. That chin of Marc's told the story, the deep cleft of tremendous will-power. She was out of his life for good.

From that day on Amanda's career progressed strikingly. She now became a professional model for the House of Martina and her lovely, faintly melancholy face looked steadily out of the covers of all the national glossies. She was determined to succeed and she worked very hard at it. But the harm was done. Her heart was encased in ice and she went around knowing she was doomed always to want a man she could never have. Though her green eyes glowed iridescent and her red lips parted in a smile, she took no pleasure in the company of the many ardent young men who imagined they could turn her blonde coolness to fire.

Life was livable, highly organised, with trips to Hong Kong and Bali and the beautiful cities of Aukland and San Francisco on location for Martina's fashion shots, but it was oddly without flavour, like a famous dish made without sauce and seasoning. Almost eighteen months to the day since Amanda had left Chandler, she was driven to the Southern Cross Hotel along with her fellow models to take part in a fashion parade/ luncheon, organised by the fantastic Lady McAllen for one of her pet charities.

Martina with her flaming red hair was there before them, and it was she who zipped Amanda into what she called her 'show-stopper', a very romantic and sexy evening dress of sheer black lace and chiffon. With it Amanda wore a breathtaking necklace and matching earrings of emeralds and diamonds that had to go back to Lady McAllen immediately the show was over.

'Beautiful, darling! You make my work a joy!' Colour touched Martina's very pale skin, showing her vulnerability to the beauty of her own creations. 'Go out there and wow 'em!'

'It's the right dress for it!' Amanda agreed, touching a reverent finger to the dazzling necklace around her throat. She moved, all soft shimmer and glitter, and her friend Liz, in her own disco dress, murmured dryly:

'You're a knock-out. What a pity you can't hold on to the jools. They never look satisfactory dangling on Alicia McAllen's billowy bosom!'

'I'm showing more than enough of mine!' Amanda returned a shade wryly. It was a fabulous dress to look at and wear, the black superb with her colouring and skin; the trouble was she was showing a little too much of it, for the brief, closely fitting bodice put the spotlight on her young exquisite breasts.

'Bare as bare can be!' Liz turned about and smiled mockingly over her shoulder. 'It's a good thing I go on before you, otherwise they won't notice me.'

'They'll notice *my dress!*' Martina called wrathfully.

Amanda smiled and patted her cheek, then moved gracefully to the side of the stage waiting her turn to walk out on the temporarily erected catwalk. She could hear the male compère's smooth pleasant voice reading out the prepared description of Martina's night-time clothes. Kim's electric blue, Liz's whirl of wine-red coloured ruffles, then he was announcing her name....

'Amanda in an extravagantly beautiful creation!'

She only moved out on to the stage when the clapping began, and to show off the lovely skirt in motion she made a few little freewheeling turns, the skirt floating away from her long slender legs. The continuing applause was everything Martina could have wanted and Amanda as she passed Lady McAllen's table gave an enchanting little bob that looked good enough to one of the waiting society photographers to snap right away.

The women's eyes followed her longingly. The attractive older women, envying her her youth; her contemporaries determined to get a little more discipline into their beauty régimes. Such a gorgeous figure, and that flawless complexion! It was impossible to look like that without working at it. The few men in the audience simply enjoyed a beautiful girl, admiring everything about her. It was important for a woman to have that little look of mystery about her, and Amanda had it.

The parade was ending more brilliantly than it had begun, and of course Martina kept her party clothes until last. Amanda was just on her final turn when she thought her mind was playing her tricks. The dazzling lights were in her eyes, but just for a moment she imagined Marc had been standing just inside the room watching her. Her heart rocked crazily and she told herself she was mistaken. She had to be mistaken, otherwise she would never make it back up the catwalk. She had seen him before, hadn't she? And every time it had turned out to be someone else. Someone quite without Marc's physical distinction and bred-in-the-bone authority.

She paled, then a wild flush spread over her cheekbones and the compère looked at her thinking he would never get used to a woman's beauty. When Liz and Kim came back on to the stage to join her she fixed her eyes on the back of the huge, flower-decorated room. There was no one. She should be used to it, the sickening lurch of heartache. Afterwards, a discerning Martina told her to go home. Fond as she was of her young protégée and star, Martina was convinced that Amanda was too fragile for words. The show had been a great success and no one had attempted to steal Alicia's famous emeralds.

Amanda took a cab home, unsettled beyond words. Marc Chandler didn't want any part of her and she

didn't want any part of him either. True to her promise, little Karin was daily in her mind, but she had
to blot out all the furious pain of love she felt for
Marc. She paid the taxi driver off at the kerb and
turned to walk up to her small but elegant apartment.
With Marc's money she could have afforded a luxury
unit somewhere overlooking the harbour, but this was
a good leafy area and it suited her idea of what she
was prepared to pay.

She had only the briefest glimpse of a man who
moved out towards her from the courtyard, but it was
enough. Her whole head went light and she seemed
to be breathing with difficulty. '*Marc!*' She stood still,
in a trance, and he moved to join her with his great
self-assurance, taking hold of her arm and looking down
at her.

'Forgive me, I didn't realise my appearance would
upset you. You've gone very white.'

'You were at the showing?' she murmured, her throat
gone dry with shock.

'Yes. I called Miss Linden's establishment and they
told me where to go. Come inside, Amanda. You can't
possibly faint here.'

'The truth is I never thought I'd see you again.' She
was trembling and she broke away from him, running
up the winding flight of stone stairs flanked by showy-
faced little gazanias in all their bright colours and on
to her private entrance.

Her slim, sensitive fingers couldn't seem to match
the key to the lock and Marc took it from her to open
the door and close it carefully after them. Now the
proportions of the tastefully furnished room came down
to claustrophobic. Amanda hurried across to the slid-

ing glass door that opened on to the small secluded terrace and immediately the breeze blew in and the scent of all the balcony plants she had bought.

'Won't you sit down?' she invited, trying to fight out of her brilliant confusion. 'Can I get you something?'

'No. Come here to me, Amanda' His voice was quiet, but it had that authoritative note she so well remembered.

'No, really, Marc! I'm making some life for myself.' She stood against the curtain, her green eyes almost panic-stricken.

He held out an imperative hand. 'Come here and tell me that.'

Her eyes focused on him with intensity, her willowy body visibly trembling. 'I never expected to hear from you. Why come now?'

'How many more dreadful months?' he asked with a deliberate terseness.

'I don't understand you.'

'You never will from there!' His eyes seemed to be touching every part of her face and body.

'You look well,' she managed to get out with a pitiful attempt at normalcy. 'I thought you'd be somehow changed, but you look as vivid as ever!'

'You know Caroline was killed in a car accident?'

'I read it in the paper,' she acknowledged with a desperate tightness.

'It *was* an accident, Amanda.'

'I never thought it was anything else!' she said, shocked by the harshness of his tone.

'Some thought it was suicide.'

'Oh God!' she moaned, and suddenly crumpled.

Marc caught her before her shuddering cry was gone

from the air, lifting her and moving back with her into an armchair. 'Don't cry, darling, don't!'

'I've been so unhappy. You have no idea!'

'Haven't I?' He tilted up her chin, holding her head fast. 'You belong to me, don't you?'

'There are too many difficulties. You can have any woman you want.'

'Then it's a frightening thought that I only want you.' He pulled her hair back to stare at the perfection of her face and slender body, the flowerlike delicacy. 'What can I tell you that you want to hear?'

'How are Karin and your mother?' It was difficult to speak normally when she was feeling the same old dangerous, unique magic.

'Waiting for your return!'

'Don't be cruel, Marc!'

He frowned and his black winged brows drew together. 'I will be if you don't come to me of your own accord. Do you often wear dresses like you had on today? The black one?'

'You didn't like it?'

He gave a twisted smile. 'Oh, I *liked* it! I just don't want you wearing dresses like that in public that's all.'

'Then your arrogance is still very much alive.'

'So's my jealousy. If you want to wear next to nothing you'll have to wear it in the privacy of our bedroom.'

'*No!*'

He gave a hard little laugh. 'Do you enjoy tormenting me?'

Amanda stared up at him and her eyes lit up with green flame. 'The same way you've tormented me all these long months!'

'You should thank me. Do you know what you look like now? A woman who's ready to be loved and love!'

She started to struggle and he held her tightly. 'I have a chance at a new life, a chance for a son. I want you and I need you and I'm going to have you. I'll even make you sleep with me, then we can discuss the whole thing afterwards when you know what you really want.'

'Have you sworn you'd never tell a woman you loved her?' she asked a little wildly.

A trace of perplexity crossed his dark face. 'Haven't I said that, my beloved little fool?'

'No, you haven't!'

It was all she managed to get out, because he gathered her up to him with a profound hunger, crushing her soft mouth, then when he met with the sudden irresistible passion of her response, he began to kiss her deeply, so that by degrees the combined tumult of their emotions merged into a single burning flame and the rightness of being together was known to both of them.

When Marc lifted his dark head an exultant light shone in the depths of his eyes. '*Now* tell me I don't love you!'

'My heart is racing madly!' she said in a small, shaky voice. 'Don't leave me, Marc. Don't ever leave me again!'

He wrapped his hand in her hair, bending to kiss her mouth again, this time with a tremendous tenderness like a life pledge. 'No one will ever separate us,' he said vibrantly, 'and no one will be allowed to try. What's happened in my life can't be changed, but it's in the past. I tried to forget you, now you're mine to have and hold. Come back with me, Amanda. Life has no meaning without you and Karin needs you badly. Together we'll be able to give her the love and stability her temperament craves. And I want a son. *Our* son. But first I want you to myself!' The hands that cupped her face conveyed strength and tenderness and a thrilling mastery. 'The first time I ever saw you I knew you'd alter my life. Strange, but I swear it's true!'

Amanda couldn't doubt he was serious. Instinctively she put up her hand, pulling his head down to her, revelling in the thick, springy feel of his hair. 'Oh, Marc!' she whispered, 'Love me so I'll know it's true!'

His hands tightened on her body, then she was lost to him as he found her young, ardent mouth.

The Warrender Saga

The most frequently requested series of Harlequin Romances . . . Mary Burchell's Warrender Saga

A Song Begins   The Curtain Rises
The Broken Wing   Song Cycle
Child of Music   Music of the Heart
Unbidden Melody
Remembered Serenade
When Love Is Blind

Each complete novel is set in the exciting world of music and opera, spanning the years from the meeting of Oscar and Anthea in *A Song Begins* to his knighthood in *Remembered Serenade*. These nine captivating love stories introduce you to a cast of characters as vivid, interesting and delightful as the glittering, exotic locations. From the tranquil English countryside to the capitals of Europe—London, Paris, Amsterdam—the Warrender Saga will sweep you along in an unforgettable journey of drama, excitement and romance.

The Warrender Saga

The most frequently requested Harlequin Romance series

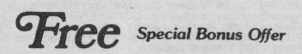

Free Special Bonus Offer

Purchase all 9 Warrender Saga novels and receive Mary Burchell's We Followed Our Stars as a Free Bonus.

We Followed Our Stars is the story of two sisters who crossed the Atlantic in the golden days of the 1920s, plunging into the glittering world of the opera . . . and later into the horrible brutality of Hitler's war-torn Europe. It's the real story of Ida Cook, a stenographer who became one of the world's most loved writers of romantic fiction— Mary Burchell.

$1.50 *if purchased separately!*

Complete and mail this coupon today!